UNWANTED WIFE

Trapped behind the Iron Curtain and separated from her husband almost immediately after their marriage, Tanya found him again, years later, believing himself free and—engaged to another girl. Could she regain his love, or was it lost to her for ever?

Books you will enjoy
by RACHEL LINDSAY

PRESCRIPTION FOR LOVE

Dominic Elton was a brilliant consultant; Vanessa Edwards was a dedicated nurse. It was inevitable that they would make a wonderful team. But soon Vanessa was having to admit to herself that she would be far happier if he would see her as a woman rather than just an efficient colleague . . .

FORBIDDEN LOVE

Venetia was not looking forward to working in Hong Kong as secretary to a neurotic, unhappily married woman. The job turned out to be even more problem-filled than she had feared—and the biggest problem of all was her employer's attractive husband . . .

A MAN TO TAME

Kate Gibson was going to have a hard struggle to persuade the man at Howard Engineering to accept her as their factory doctor. And the forceful head of the firm, Joshua Howard, was going to be another problem. Did she want him to see her as a doctor—or as a woman?

THE MARQUIS TAKES A WIFE

David Cecil Edward Thomas York, Marquis of Powys, was more interested in his research work in Africa than in settling down at his family seat and producing an heir—much to his grandmother's distress. So she went out to join him in Africa with her young companion Beth Miller, to see if she could talk him around. And in the process Beth became more involved with the Marquis and his romantic life than she had bargained for . . .

UNWANTED WIFE

BY
RACHEL LINDSAY

MILLS & BOON LIMITED
17–19 FOLEY STREET
LONDON W1A 1DR

All the characters in this book have no existence outside the imagination of the Author, and have no relation whatsoever to anyone bearing the same name or names. They are not even distantly inspired by any individual known or unknown to the Author, and all the incidents are pure invention. The text of this publication or any part thereof may not be reproduced or transmitted in any form or by any means, electronic or mechanical, including photocopying, recording, storage in an information retrieval system, or otherwise, without the written permission of the publisher.

A revised version of
A TIME TO LOVE by Janey Scott, first published 1960

Australian copyright 1978
Philippine copyright 1978
This edition 1978

This edition © Rachel Lindsay 1978

For copyright reasons, this book may not be issued on loan or otherwise except in its original soft cover.

ISBN 0 263 72699 1

Set in Linotype Times 10 on 11½ pt.

Made and printed in Great Britain by
Richard Clay (The Chaucer Press), Ltd., Bungay, Suffolk

CHAPTER ONE

ADRIAN CHESTERTON picked up his pen, leaned forward on his desk and began to sign the last of his letters. The light from the ormolu desk lamp picked out the burnished glints in his light brown hair and gave his skin—normally pale—a warmer hue. But as he straightened, the warmth vanished, leaving him looking pale and composed; which he invariably was.

'There you are,' he smiled, closing the folder and passing it to his middle-aged secretary. 'You can't complain I don't keep pace with my post.'

'Only because you work far too long hours,' she smiled back. 'I don't know how you'd manage without tape recorders.'

'By having another paragon like you—if that were possible,' he replied, and rose to walk to the door, a tall, slimly built man in his mid-thirties.

His upright bearing brought to mind his military ancestors and a patrician fineness of features left one in little doubt that the Edwardian rumours of a Scandinavian prince having a close relationship with a Chesterton wife could well have been true. He was, as an acute observer could see, a man of contradictions. Finely arched brows, so rigidly marked they could have been sculpted on, were at variance with the sensitive cut of his mouth, glacial blue eyes had their coldness redeemed by the soft frond of lashes that framed them, and the square jaw of a man of action was contradicted by the wide brow of a thinker.

5

Crossing the hall to the drawing-room, he found his mother waiting to join him in their usual pre-dinner drink. Mrs Chesterton, grey-haired and regal, was seated on a gilt chair looking through the marriage columns of *The Times*. He handed her a glass of dry sherry and she looked up and spoke.

'Nigel Lockheed is marrying Bruce Cardley's daughter. That explains why he joined Cardley's bank last year.'

Adrian shrugged and crossed the room to switch on the radio. A news bulletin was in progress, but as he went to listen, his mother waved her hand impatiently.

'Do turn it off. I want to talk to you.'

Her tone left him in no doubt about the subject. 'Not Diana again,' he said a trifle impatiently, and lowered the volume without switching off.

'Can you blame me?' Mrs Chesterton asked. 'I don't know what's the matter with you both. You've been engaged four months and you still haven't set a date for the wedding.'

'There's no rush.'

'Anyone would think you don't want to get married,' she persisted.

'Then they'd be wrong.'

'Which you can prove by setting the date. Or is it Diana who's prevaricating?'

'Neither of us is prevaricating,' he said calmly. 'It just so happens we aren't in a hurry.'

His mother frowned. 'Have you already presumed upon your vows?'

For an instant her son looked blank, then he gave a tight smile. 'No, Mother, we haven't. Though even if we had, it wouldn't make marriage unnecessary.'

'It might make it less urgent.' There was no reply, but

Mrs Chesterton remained undeterred. 'You've been single for so long, you've become monkish. It's time you had a wife and family.'

'Once the by-election is over, we'll fix a date.' He pursed his lips. 'I won't want a big wedding, Mother. This isn't my first marriage, you know.'

'It's Diana's *first*, and she has a right to expect something special. As for your other wedding—well, you know what I thought about *that*. A hole-and-corner affair with a little foreigner who——'

'Mother!'

'I'm sorry, Adrian, but every time I think of the way she behaved . . .'

'She had no choice.' Still holding his drink, he went to the door. 'I have a few more things to do. I'll see you at dinner.'

Swiftly he returned to the library, a large, rectangular room whose warm brown furnishings were reflected in the mahogany desk and bookshelves. This was the place where he felt most at peace. Standing by the window, he looked out over the neat lawns, seeing in his mind's eye the acres of rolling pastureland that lay beyond it. It was all his and he loved every inch of it; loved the people who worked it and for whom he was responsible. In one respect his mother was right: he needed a wife to share in the joy and responsibility of ownership; needed children who would grow up to feel the same and take over from him when he was too old to continue.

A picture of Tanya flashed into his mind: the tall slender girl he had married eight years ago. She had been eighteen then, shy and nervous and with the blonde colouring of her race: honey-gold hair to complement pale golden skin and violet eyes. He had not believed anyone could have eyes of that particular shade and, on first seeing them, had thought they reflected the colour of her dress. Afterwards he had realised this was not so, for no matter what she wore her eyes still remained that glorious and unusual shade of deep violet.

How long ago it seemed! Eight years in time yet a lifetime away in experience. Remembering the youth he had once been, Adrian felt as though he were thinking of a stranger. But that youth was indeed a stranger, bearing little resemblance to the man of today—mature and austere—who resigned from the Foreign Office to take over his father's estate, and who was soon to marry the daughter of Lord Biddell.

He tried to keep his mind fixed on the present but, having loosened hold of his memories, was no longer master of them, and an image of Tanya, as he had first seen her, came to the forefront of his mind.

It had been a glorious day in midsummer and it was also his first experience of a Rovnian festival, for he had only recently arrived at the British Embassy at Rovnik. Together with friends he had gone to the town centre to watch the Rose Carnival, a traditional pageant that went so far back in history no one could remember its original meaning. Not that anybody seemed to care: to the youth of Rovnia one excuse to celebrate was as good as another.

The festivities took the form of dancing in the street, toasting each other in Vassi, a light sweet wine of the region, and cheering the gaily decorated carts laden with roses of every variety and colour, which paraded through the main street.

It was after watching the tenth rose-laden cart that his attention had wandered and his eyes, roaming the happy crowd, had lighted upon the tall, slender girl standing with a group of her compatriots to one side of the main square. Like her friends, she wore the traditional Rov-nian costume of wide swinging skirt and gaily embroid-ered blouse, but unlike her friends she was not cheering and waving but watching the carts with a look of thoughtfulness on her fine-boned face. Had she been nearer Adrian would have strolled over to try to find out why she should look so sad when everyone around her was happy, but as the thought crossed his mind she was lost to sight in a surging mass of people, and when they moved on, so had the girl.

By late afternoon he had had his fill of food and drink and, unwilling to join in the street dancing which was now occupying his friends, he made his excuses and decided to return home. This was easier said than done, for the streets were still packed and he was frequently brought to a halt by boisterous strangers who tried to persuade him to join in their revelry. It was after he had refused the fifth offer and was edging his way towards a narrow alleyway that would lead him to the Embassy that he saw the pensive blonde girl again. This time she was caught up in a crowd of young dancers and ap-peared to be enjoying herself. But as he watched, the dancing grew more boisterous and he saw she was find-ing it difficult to keep pace with those around her. She tried to pull away from them, but her hands were too tightly held for her to free herself and, as the swinging procession veered towards him, he reached out and caught her round the waist. For an instant he was not sure he could retain his hold on her, then she was sud-denly free of the crowd and standing beside him on the pavement slightly protected by the alley directly behind them. Briefly he remained holding her, then with a quick apology he let her go and she smoothed her skirt and blouse self-consciously.

'Are you all right?' he asked, his poor Rovnian unmistakably marking him a foreigner.

'Yes, thank you. It was kind of you to rescue me.'

She made to move away and it was then that he surprised himself, for he was not by nature an impetuous young man. But there was something about this girl that made him want to know her better, and he stepped in front of her to bar her way.

'I know a quiet restaurant near here. If you would let me buy you a drink . . .' He saw her hesitation and said : 'I can give you impeccable references if you wish. My name is Adrian Chesterton and I work at the British Embassy.'

'I am Tanya Kovacs.' She had held out her hand shyly and he had taken it with a smile.

'Now we've been properly introduced,' he continued, 'I hope it's in order for you to have an iced chocolate with me!'

That had been the beginning of their friendship, though it had quickly ripened into something far deeper. Highly intelligent and well-educated, Tanya was by no means like the liberated young English girls to whom he was accustomed. Born late in life to middle-aged parents, she had acquired from them a different set of values from those of her young friends, though, as she had candidly admitted, they were values that frequently made her feel a stranger with her own generation.

'But I wouldn't change one moment of my upbringing,' she had added. 'My father is a historian, you know, and I have learned more from him than from anyone else. To him the past is as real as the present—sometimes I think it's more real, and then I become afraid for him.'

There had been no need for Adrian to ask her what

she meant, political events in Rovnia had made it all too
clear. Those who remembered the past—when freedom
of speech had gone hand in hand with every other civil
liberty—could not help but compare it unfavourably
with the military state that Rovnia was today: a land
where wine flowed free but where thoughts were stifled.

But in those warm summer days the darkening political situation had not been uppermost in Adrian's mind.
All he could think of was making Tanya his wife. Surprisingly, the Ambassador put little obstacle in his way,
nor did the Rovnian Government make objections when
one of their nationals applied to marry a foreigner. The
intellectual standing of Tanya's father no doubt had
something to do with their attitude, for Professor Kovacs
was known in academic circles throughout the world. Not
that Adrian would have cared if her father had been an
illiterate peasant; it was Tanya he loved; Tanya with
whom he wished to spend his life.

It was while they were on honeymoon that the political situation in the country worsened. There was a *coup
d'état* and the Prime Minister was superseded by a
military dictator. Adrian was recalled to England and
ten days after their marriage, Tanya kissed him goodbye
at the airport.

'I'll be with you soon, my darling,' she had whispered.
'In a week my papers and passport will be in order and
I'll follow you.'

'I'll count the hours.' Adrian had hugged her fiercely,
and neither of them had imagined they would never see
each other again.

At first Tanya had not come to England because her
father was imprisoned and she had refused to leave her
mother alone, then as doubts for his father-in-law's
safety began to fill his mind, Adrian had pleaded with

her to leave Rovnia while she was still able to do so. Twice he spoke to her on the telephone, but she became progressively more reticent and he had been forced to read what he could into her silences. Then a letter came from her saying her father had died in prison and she had applied for permission to take her mother to England. His delight was short-lived, for a visa was refused—and worse, Tanya's own visa was cancelled.

Without success Adrian pestered the Embassy in London, but always met with the same answer: his letters to his wife were being delivered and if she did not reply to him and refused to take his telephone calls, it was her own wish and no one else's. Refusing to believe this, he fought continually for her release, even though, in all that time, there was no word from her. Then a day before their second wedding anniversary, the Rovnian Government announced that all their citizens who had married foreigners had requested their marriages to be dissolved.

'I don't believe my wife would do such a thing of her own free will,' he had stormed at the Rovnian attaché he had managed to see. 'You must have pressurised her into it.'

But none of his comments evoked a response, and it was only when his superior at the Foreign Office advised him that it would be in Tanya's own interest for him to stop making a nuisance of himself at the Embassy that he had realised he might be putting her life in danger.

It was no easy decision for him to accept that his marriage was over, but as time passed he had wondered if her silence in that first year had been deliberate. Perhaps she hadn't wanted to leave her country? Surely if she had, she could have found a way of escape? Gradually these questions became statements in his mind. No

longer did he surmise about Tanya; it was as if he knew
for sure and, in the knowing, his love began to ebb.

The death of his father undoubtedly helped him to put
his abortive marriage firmly into the past, for it caused
him to resign from his job and take over the running of
the family estate. Gradually he settled back into a rural
existence, finding a peace and tranquillity there he had
thought forever lost.

The years piled one upon another until six months
ago, he had realised he not only had an inheritance to
take care of but also one to preserve for the future; to
this end he had proposed to Diana Biddell, an elegant
dark-haired girl with a cool manner, whom he had
known since childhood. He had no illusions that theirs
was a great love match. She liked him—as he liked
her—and their marriage would be based on mutual interests which would enable them to share their future
amicably.

In the months following his engagement, the Member
of Parliament for their district died, and Adrian was
asked to take his place. Had it been for any other constituency he would have refused, but he was keenly
interested in the farming community and decided to fight
for their rights. Trinton was by no means a safe seat and
he knew he had a tough battle on his hands in order to
win against his opponent, Roger Poulton, a red-haired
young man with a fiery disposition, whose family had
lived in the village for generations. Poulton had worked
his way through college and, though now a lecturer at a
neighbouring university, saw himself as the working
man's crusader.

'I won't be a part-time M.P.,' was his favourite elec-
tioneering comment, which skilfully cast doubt on
whether Adrian would be too preoccupied with his own

affairs as a landowner to worry sufficiently about his
constituents. It was a slur that Adrian had been quick to
demolish, but always Poulton came back again and
again with fighting words.

A knock at the door made him turn from the window
as a stocky young man with a weatherbeaten face came
in.

'Am I disturbing you, Adrian?'

'Not at all. Come in and take a pew. Anything to
report?'

Dick Tufton—who was his brother-in-law as well as
his estate manager—sat in an armchair and stuck his
legs out in front of him. 'Old man Grant's complaining
about his roof again. We've repaired it twice this year
already—I swear he sits up at night poking holes in the
ceiling!'.

Adrian chuckled. 'You'd better fix it for him.'

'You're too easy-going,' Dick replied. 'He's a cantankerous old devil and you shouldn't give in to him.'

'Being eighty years old is enough to make anyone
cantankerous! Anything else worrying you?'

'Nothing I can't take care of myself. I only told you
about Grant as an item of news!'

'Who needs news?'

Dick pulled a face. 'I wish you'd say that in front of
Betty. At the moment she's griping that nothing ever
happens here.'

'Perhaps she's bored. Why not go out for dinner tonight?'

'I'm too tired. Betty would be tired too if she did a
proper day's work.'

Adrian said nothing. He knew Dick did not like living
with his wife's family, but felt it was something they
must resolve between themselves.

'Let's go in and have a drink,' he said diplomatically.

Dick went with him to the door. 'Diana coming over tonight?'

'Yes. She's probably here now.'

As he spoke, Adrian opened the drawing-room door. Diana and his mother were sitting together on the settee and the younger woman looked up at him with a smile. He went over to kiss her smooth cheek, thinking how nice she looked in a simple navy dress.

'How about taking a drive after dinner?' he murmured, his pulses stirring at the smell of the scent she used.

'That would be lovely. If you——' She stopped as the elderly butler came in and stood beside Adrian.

'Excuse me, Mr Chesterton, but there's a young lady to see you.'

'At this time of night?' his mother interjected.

'Who is it, Hamford?' Adrian asked.

'She wouldn't give her name, sir. Just said she has to see you.'

'Well, you'd better show her in.' The butler went out and Adrian looked at his fiancée. 'It's probably an election canvasser with a message.'

The door opened and a woman in an ill-fitting black coat came in. A scarf in motley shades of blue all but hid a few untidy wisps of hair, while down-at-heel shoes covered her feet. In one hand she carried a misshapen handbag and in the other a battered suitcase, which she set down on the carpet.

For a moment the three people in the room stared at her, then Adrian took a step forward.

'I believe you wished to see me,' he said courteously.

The woman stared at him and the soft glow of a standard lamp nearby fell upon her features. They had an angular thinness that came from lack of food rather than inherited shape, and confirmation for this could be seen in the greyish pallor of the skin tightly stretched over the high cheekbones. It was difficult to guess her age, but Adrian was sure that with adequate nourishment and rest she would look considerably younger than she did at the moment.

'Adrian!' His name came from between her lips, a bare sliver of sound that cut the air between them as though it were a laser beam.

He frowned. 'I'm afraid I don't...' The rest of his sentence died as a dreadful suspicion filtered into his mind. He went on staring at her, as if the intensity of his gaze would cause her to melt away. But she remained a fixed image in front of him: a thin creature of indeterminate age in shabby black clothes. But it was her hands that horrified him the most, for he remembered them as white and delicate, and they were now roughened and red from work, the nails broken, the fingers moving convulsively. It was the sight of those writhing fingers that awakened him to a sense of his responsibility.

'Tanya!' he whispered. 'Is it ... You can't be Tanya!'

Hearing him say her name, the woman gave a harsh sob and flung herself at his chest. Awkwardly he patted her shoulder, at the same time looking over her head to where his mother and Diana were staring at him in horror. But it was nothing to the horror he felt within himself.

'It's—my—er—it's Tanya,' he said aloud. 'She must have escaped and—and come straight here.'

'Oh, my poor Adrian!' His mother's voice rose. 'Whatever are we going to do?'

CHAPTER TWO

FOR as long as she lived, Tanya would never forget the first time she found herself alone with Adrian in his home.

After his mother's horrified question, Adrian had led her into another smaller room whose atmosphere of intimacy went some little way towards restoring her confidence. But the confidence ebbed swiftly when Adrian quickly stepped away from her and motioned her to sit down, carefully placing himself some distance away.

'I wish you'd let me know you were coming,' he said jerkily. 'It was a—a shock to see you.' He paused, as though uncertain how to go on, then said: 'I take it you've come straight from Rovnia?'

'Yes. I could not let you know because the arrangements were made so quickly.'

'You were lucky to escape,' he said tonelessly. 'Not many of your countrymen do.'

'But many wish they could. You know my people, Adrian. You can imagine how much they hate the régime.'

'They've lived with it for eight years.'

'Eight years of fighting. There is still great resistance. What you would call here—an underground.'

'I've read about it,' he said, 'but one is never sure how true it is.'

'It is all true,' she said vehemently. 'I should know, for I was in it myself.' She paused, wondering why they should be talking like this when there were so many other things they should be saying. She was with Adrian —her husband—the man she loved with all her heart. Her eyes searched his face, seeing how the years had changed it and knowing that the boy who had kissed her goodbye at the airport was now a man. The slight diffidence in his manner had been replaced by an air of command and the soft-spoken voice had a firmer ring to it. But basically he was still the same. That Adrian was not thinking this about *her* was obvious from the way he was watching her; as if he were looking at someone he had never seen before.

'When did you leave Rovnia?' he asked.

'Three days ago. But even after I was across the border, I had to be careful. I was in hiding for twenty-four hours and then I was put aboard a train.'

'What are your plans?' he asked stiltedly.

'My plans?' She looked at him blankly. 'What plans should I have? I have come here to you. You are my husband.'

'Not any longer,' he stated. 'You divorced me six years ago.'

'What?' Tanya jumped up. 'It is not true. You are lying!'

'I'm not. Six years ago your government announced that all their citizens who were married to foreigners had divorced them.'

'You must have known I would never do that!'

'How could I have known?' He saw her sway and compassion made him step forward and gently place her back in her chair. 'Surely you *knew* about it, Tanya? I didn't blame you for it. I realised you had no choice and——'

'I knew nothing about it,' she cried. 'All I knew was that my letters to you were never answered—that my attempts to get in touch with you came to nothing. It was as though you were dead. I was never told anything about a divorce. Never! All the time we've been apart I have lived for the moment when I would see you ... when I would be with you...'

She burst into sobs again and he patted her shoulder awkwardly. 'Please don't cry. You're in England and quite safe. I'm sorry if my greeting was rather constrained, but seeing you was something of a shock.'

Something of a shock. The words were such an understatement that they almost made her laugh. Except that she was the butt of the joke. Not only was she a foreigner in an alien country, but the man to whom she had come no longer wanted her. Worse than that, for five years he had believed she no longer wanted *him*.

Carefully she searched his face, trying to read his thoughts from his expression. But he gave nothing away and she felt as if she were looking at a stranger. Yet he wasn't a stranger. He was still the man she had married; still the man whose ring she wore.

'Naturally you will stay here until you have decided what you want to do,' Adrian said. 'If there's any way I can help you——'

'I want nothing from you,' she burst out. 'Nothing!'

'You're only saying that because you're upset. I still feel responsible for you and I want to take care of you.'

'I don't want care,' she cried. 'I want love!'

'I don't think either of us should talk about love. It's eight years since we saw one another and in that time we've changed.'

'Not me,' she said bitterly. 'I am the same. Always the same.' Her hands fluttered upwards. 'Have you forgotten the past so quickly? Doesn't seeing me again make you remember how you felt about me?'

Jerkily he turned away from her. 'No. No, it doesn't.

Six years ago you divorced me. Knowing that changed the way I felt. I'm sorry, Tanya, but there's no point hiding the truth from you.'

Tanya tried to hold herself aloof from his words, but painfully, heartbreakingly, they seeped into her. 'You mean you no longer love me?'

'I'm saying we're two different people from the man and the girl who married each other eight years ago. Our parting was not something we wanted to happen, but it did happen and—and we can't turn back the clock.'

For a long moment she was silent, twisting her hands together, feeling her wedding ring. 'Is it because I am no longer beautiful that you do not love me?'

'Oh, God!' The words were forced from him. 'Don't say that to me. It's got nothing to do with the way you look.'

'Yes, it has,' she said. 'I am a stranger to you. I can see that now.' She stood up again and, doing so, glimpsed herself in the gold-framed mirror above the marble mantelshelf. 'Yes,' she reiterated, 'when I look at myself I can see the face of an old woman. Old before my time.' She crossed to the door. 'It is not necessary to talk any more. I will go.'

'Go where?'

'To London. I am afraid to go the Rovnian Embassy, but there must be a hostel where——'

'Don't be absurd! You must stay here until we have made plans. I know it isn't what you expected it would be, but at least be sensible.'

'Sensible,' she echoed. 'That is a word you use a lot. Very well, Adrian, what is the sensible thing you wish me to do?'

'Right now you should go to bed. You look exhausted.'

'I have not slept since I left Rovnia,' she admitted.

'Then I'll—then my mother will show you to your room and see you settled. After a good night's rest things will look different. I suggest we leave any further discussion until then.'

'A very sensible suggestion,' she said sedately, and if he saw the mockery in her use of the word, he gave no indication of it.

'I'll have dinner sent up to you on a tray,' he said.

'I'm not hungry.'

'You may feel like something to eat when you've had a bath and a rest.'

Without answering she preceded him into the hall. She could not face going into the drawing-room and hovered on the threshold while he spoke to his mother. She was too far away to hear what he said, but she saw the woman's anxiety as she rose and came towards her.

'I think it very wise of Adrian to suggest you go to bed. You must be tired after your exhausting journey.'

Not trusting herself to speak, Tanya nodded and followed her mother-in-law up the graceful flight of stairs to the first floor. But the woman walking so rigidly erect in front of her was no longer her mother-in-law, for she herself was no longer Adrian's wife. She was a stranger in a strange house; unwanted and knowing it. The sooner she left the better.

Early morning sunshine filtered into the bedroom and Tanya lay back among the pillows and looked round the beautifully furnished room. A soft green carpet covered the floor, its colour picked out in the flowered chintz curtains that made a more vivid splash of colour against the cream walls. On a rosewood table beside her bed stood a tray with some half-eaten food on it: the remains of the dinner Adrian had sent up to her last night.

Adrian ... She could not think of that forbidding man downstairs as the same man she had married. Through the long years of their separation she had kept his memory alive in her heart, but when memory had come face to face with reality, it was the past which had ceased to exist.

Was it because she had expected him to remain as he had been on the day they had kissed one another good-bye? But no, to say that was to be too kind to him. She had been prepared to find him changed, grown older, made harder by time. What she had not anticipated was that the Adrian of today would make the man of eight years ago seem a total stranger.

How coldly he had looked at her! The horror had been quickly masked, but the incredulity had remained; so had the aloofness with which he had put his hands on her shoulders, their light touch showing no lover-like quality; only a recoil which they tried hard to disguise.

Tanya jumped out of bed and peered at her image in the dressing-table mirror. She saw a hollow-cheeked face with large eyes. The skin was still clear but without a trace of colour; the blonde hair so devoid of lustre that it looked greyish. She could not blame Adrian for not recognising her. Sometimes she hardly recognised herself. Sighing, she began to dress.

She was coming out of the private bathroom which adjoined her bedroom when a maid came in with a breakfast tray.

'Good morning, miss.' She placed the tray on the bedside table. 'I hope you slept well?'

'Yes, thank you.' Tanya looked at the coffee and rolls. 'I am ready to go down for breakfast.'

'Mr Chesterton asked me to bring it up to you. He

also said he would like to see you in the library as soon as it is convenient.'

'I'll go now.' Tanya made a move, but the girl shook her head.

'I shouldn't hurry, miss. Have your breakfast first—it will do you good.'

Tanya hesitated, then realising the truth of the remark, perched on the edge of the bed and poured herself some coffee.

It tasted delicious after the synthetic brew to which she had become accustomed in Rovnia; so did the crisp rolls and creamy butter. But she could not eat with appetite and, thinking of the interview ahead, wished it were already over. But the maid had told her not to hurry, and she forced herself to have another cup of coffee, then wandered back to the dressing-table and listlessly combed her hair.

Used as she was to wearing old unfashionable clothes, it was only among these elegant surroundings that she realised how shabby she looked. Her black serge skirt hung almost to her ankles and her blouse had been washed so many times that the brilliant coloured embroidery for which her country was famous had faded. But there was nothing she could do about it, and when she had pinned her hair into its customary neat roll at the back of her head, she went to the library, as Adrian had requested.

He rose from his desk as she went in. 'I hope you slept well?' he asked politely.

'Yes, thank you.' Without waiting to be asked, she sat down. 'I do not think we have much to discuss. The sooner I leave, the better.'

'It isn't as simple as that. I've already had a call from

someone in the village enquiring if you'd arrived here safely.'

'Enquiring?'

'You asked several people the way to get here last night,' he replied. 'One of them happened to be the village gossip—who also has the memory of an elephant. She remembered I was once married to a foreign girl and she——'

'Guessed I was your wife?' Tanya cut in breathlessly.

'Not that,' he said with a shake of his head. 'Though if we do anything to make her suspicious she might well put two and two together. At the moment she thinks you came here to—to . . .' He paused, as though finding it difficult to say what he wanted and then, giving up the struggle, said instead: 'I'm not ashamed of having married you, Tanya. I want you to believe that.'

'If you say so.'

'I do say so.' For the first time there was emotion in his voice. 'I loved you very much and I only wish that—that things could have worked out differently.'

'Thank you. I am glad you said that.'

For several seconds they gazed at one another, then Adrian blinked his eyes rapidly, as if trying not to see the past. 'There's something else you should know,' he went on. 'I'm standing for Parliament, and if it leaks out that I've a wife who comes from behind the Iron Curtain, it could be disastrous for me.'

'Why? Anyway, I am no longer your wife.'

'I'm not so sure about that. The fact that our divorce was decreed by your government doesn't mean it's valid in this country—especially as we were married at the British Embassy.'

'I'm sure you will be able to arrange things to suit you.'

He nodded, not commenting on her sarcasm. 'There

won't be any problem. I'd intended to sort it out once the election was over.'

'I still do not understand why my coming here could harm you. My father was imprisoned and murdered because he did not agree with the régime, and I had to be smuggled out of the country for the same reason.'

'Intelligent people would realise that,' he replied. 'But they're not all intelligent.'

'Is that the only reason you wish to hide my identity? I do not have great command of your language, but that should not make you think I am retarded. And last night I sensed there was another reason why my arrival here was so unwelcome to you.'

'If I was hiding anything,' he said swiftly, 'it was done merely not to hurt you.'

'I am used to hurt. Please go on.'

There was a pause. 'Do you recollect the girl sitting on the settee next to my mother?' he asked at last.

'The one with dark hair? I thought she was your sister.'

'No. My sister was still upstairs. The girl you saw was—is—my fiancée.'

Tanya swallowed hard. 'How can you be engaged when you told me you do not consider yourself free?'

'Of course I'm free. As I just told you, it's only a matter of legalising the position.'

'It's a pity you did not do it six years ago. Then you would not have to bother with me today.'

'You aren't a bother,' he replied. 'You were my wife and I have a duty to look after you.'

'I would prefer to leave. I am used to fending for myself. My mother was ill for many years after my father died, and the authorities made it difficult for me to find work. Even our friends were afraid to show their closeness to us, and I learned then how to cope on my own.'

'Why didn't you try to escape before?' he asked.

'I could not leave while my mother was alive.'

Adrian coloured. 'I'm sorry. I should have realised that. But now you're here, I wish you to stay until . . .'

His voice trailed away, but Tanya knew what he had left unsaid. 'Until your election is over?'

'Yes. Already everybody in the village knows you're here, and if you go away so soon they'll wonder why.'

'Tell them I was a new maid,' she said lightly, 'and that I was not adequate.' His sudden flush made her stare at him harder. 'Is that what—what you want me to pretend I am?'

'No, no, not that.' His voice was sharp. 'But nurse to my sister's children. As a pretence only, of course. My mother suggested it as a way out of the problem. Then you could remain here until I arrange to take care of you properly.'

'If I stay, it is only because I do not wish to affect your career. I want nothing from you.'

'We'll talk about that later.' He avoided her eyes. 'You're being extremely co-operative, Tanya.'

'Do not thank me. Beggars cannot be choosers, and in the home of my husband I am truly a beggar.'

'My dear, don't say that!'

Ignoring the anguish in his voice, because her own anguish was the greater, she fled from the room.

Alone in the hall she stared round with a hunted expression, then pushed open the door directly opposite her and found herself in the room she had first entered last night. It was beautifully furnished with the understated elegance that typified all she had so far seen of the house. Huge bowls of garden flowers perfumed the air and french windows stood wide open to show a view of a York stone terrace. Tanya made for this at once and did not pause until she had reached the shallow steps that led down to the lawn. This too was everything she had supposed an English lawn to be: smooth, flower-bordered and a perfection of green. In the distance a small plantation of silver birches pointed to a lily pond. Overwhelmed by the unexpected beauty, her eyes filled with tears, but she blinked them away, knowing it would be fatal if she allowed herself to be overwhelmed by self-pity. She must not think how different her future was going to be from all she had hoped for. Instead she must think how different it was going to be from her past. She might not have Adrian, but at least she had her freedom.

The branch of a tree brushed against her hair and she looked up, enthralled by the loveliness of cherry blossom. She could not restrain a murmur of joy and she pulled a laden branch down and pressed her face against them.

'They *are* gorgeous, aren't they?' said a voice, and Tanya turned to see a girl of about her own age, with short chestnut hair and a pleasant if unremarkable face. 'You must be Tanya,' the girl went on. 'I'm Betty Tufton, Adrian's sister.'

'Adrian has spoken of you,' Tanya said. 'I am to look after your children, I think.'

'That's just a ploy to stop the gossips putting two and two together and making five,' Betty said quickly. 'Though if it had been left to me, I'd have told them the truth.'

'The truth would have harmed Adrian.'

'I don't agree. But unfortunately no one takes any notice of me.'

Betty did not seem distressed by this and Tanya had

the impression it would take a great deal to disturb her.

'I suppose one can't blame Adrian for wanting to make absolutely sure nothing spoils his chances at the election,' his sister went on, 'but it's a bit much to expect you to look after my brats.'

'I will certainly take care of your children,' Tanya said formally. 'It is what Adrian wishes.'

'Did you always do as he wished?' Betty Tufton asked, and then gave an embarrassed laugh. 'Don't answer that!'

'I would answer you if I could, but your brother and I were not together long enough for me to do so.'

'Of course. I was forgetting he had to leave you when you were practically on your honeymoon. It must have been ghastly for you.'

'The last eight years were not pleasant ones either,' Tanya answered. 'I think it is better if we do not talk about them.'

'It's no good to bottle things up.'

'Sometimes it is safer.'

'Less embarrassing, you mean?' Betty Tufton gave her a long, appraising look. 'When you smiled at me a moment ago I was able to see the girl Adrian married. For the first year after he got back he didn't stop telling us how beautiful you were.'

'That is in the past too. Today I am ugly.' Tanya glanced at her shapeless dress and work-roughened hands. 'It is hard for me to realise I am no longer his wife. I knew nothing about the divorce.'

Betty was astounded. 'You must have had quite a shock when Adrian told you.'

'I did. But that is in the past also and now I am your nanny.'

Betty eyed her again. 'If I were in your shoes I think

I'd want to give Adrian a good sharp kick!'

'If you had been in my shoes for the last eight years, you would have learned the importance of hiding your true feelings.'

In silence, they continued to walk across the lawn, automatically heading in the direction of the house.

'You're still beautiful, you know,' the English girl said abruptly. 'All you need is to gain some weight and wear decent clothes.'

'Such things are unimportant to me.'

'Well, they shouldn't be. You're free now and there's no reason for you to go around looking as if you've escaped from a concentration camp.'

'But I have.'

'All the more reason to forget it! You're about my size and I'm sure I can find you something decent to wear.'

'I cannot accept charity,' persisted Tanya.

'There's no such thing as charity between sisters-in-law! And until Adrian legalises his divorce, that's what you still are. So stop arguing!'

Half smiling, Tanya shrugged acquiescence. 'Do you not have a home of your own?' she asked as she followed Betty up to the first floor and along the corridor to what was obviously a self-contained wing.

'No, I live here. When I married, Adrian was still at the Foreign Office and Mother was lonely by herself. Dick and I moved in as a temporary measure and have stayed on ever since.'

'Would you not prefer to live alone with your husband?'

'I've stopped thinking about it. Anyway, it's very convenient not to have to do any cooking.'

'Your mother cooks, then?'

Betty chuckled. 'She can't even boil an egg. No, we have a cook.'

'I see.'

'I'm sure you don't.' Betty chuckled again. 'But come on, let's start the transformation.'

True to her word, that was exactly what Betty did to Tanya. Using a strong lemon rinse, she brought back golden glints to the drab hair and snipped some of the front strands so that they fell in soft waves over Tanya's brow, leaving the rest of her hair to be wound into a thick plait and twisted round her head.

'I hope you won't refuse to wear make-up?' Betty questioned, and without waiting for an answer proceeded to dab different colours and textures on to Tanya's face.

Luckily she was as skilful as she was determined, and when Tanya studied her reflection she had difficulty in recognising herself. Though nothing could hide her thinness, the dress Betty had given her did much to minimise it. The pintucked bodice emphasised the delicate curve of her breasts yet at the same time hid the hollows at the base of her neck; the softly floating skirt was kind to the boniness of her thighs and drew attention only to the incredibly tiny waist. But it was her face which had altered the most: at last she looked as she had once been; as she knew she could look again, were she given the chance. The merest touch of rouge emphasised her high cheekbones and some lotion had been dabbed on to hide the shadows beneath her eyes. The eyes themselves were untouched except for a coat of mascara on the dark fringe of lashes, and they shone like the large violets that grew on her native hills.

'You'll look even better when you've gained ten pounds,' Betty said. 'But you look a thousand times better that you did last night. Adrian won't know you.'

Tanya's pleasure evaporated. In the company of this friendly girl she had forgotten her true position, but now it came back to haunt her. Her tears could not be controlled, and with a gasp she ran to the haven of her own room and flung herself on the bed. How could she live in this family and pretend she was a stranger to its master? How could she forget those few glorious weeks of love that they had shared? But to forget was a necessity, for unless she did, she would wreck Adrian's life.

'Give me the strength to stay,' she whispered, hands clasped together in pleading. 'And then please, please God, give me the strength to go.'

CHAPTER THREE

As the days passed, the effects of good food and rest showed markedly on Tanya. She no longer had need of rouge and her body began to regain its rounded contours.

After the first few difficult days she started to build a place for herself in the household. She and Betty's children took to each other on sight and she had a special place in her affections for five-year-old Emma, whose blonde curls and solemn little face reminded her of herself at the same age. Three-year-old Tim was a different proposition; high-spirited, very intelligent and using both characteristics in order to get his own way, he was a handful to manage. But Tanya welcomed anything that stopped her from thinking about her own problems and with Tim to watch over, was given little chance of moping.

The family treated her carefully and though she had anticipated having her meals in the nursery with the children, Adrian refused to allow this.

'But I would prefer to eat with the children,' she had protested.

'And I would prefer you to eat with us.'

In the end they compromised, Tanya agreeing to take her meals with the family when Adrian was present and, on the occasions when he wasn't, eating in the nursery. It was these mealtimes she enjoyed the most, for in the main dining room she was constantly aware of Mrs Chesterton's frigid politeness and Adrian's determined

effort to pretend they were friends, and to forget they
had once been considerably closer.

Betty and Dick Tufton behaved the most naturally
towards her and would have been pleased to take her
with them when they went to the local cinema or to visit
friends. But Tanya refused to allow this, reminding them
that since she was supposed to be their nanny it would
look strange if she went out with them socially.

Reluctantly conceding that she was right, they left her
alone, and gradually everyone else did the same. Busy
with his election campaign, Adrian no longer insisted
she dine with the family when he was present, and they
met only at Sunday luncheon, which the children took
with their parents.

The weeks merged into each other and one midsummer evening after she had put the children to bed, Tanya
went into the garden for a stroll. The day had been
humid and she breathed the cool, scented air with relief.
Sitting on the edge of the lily pond, which was her
favourite place, she leaned over and dabbled her fingers
in the water. Her face stared at her from the unrippled
surface, the sinking sun picking out the highlights in her
corn-gold hair and making it look as if the water were
flecked with gold dust.

'I didn't recognise you as I was coming across the
lawn,' Adrian said behind her, and with a startled movement she turned to see him coming towards her.

'You look different,' he went on, his eyes travelling
down her body in its tight-fitting cream linen dress, to
her bare brown legs and slim feet thrust into red sandals.

'Have I changed so much, then?' she asked stiltedly.

'Yes. Both from the girl I met in Rovnia and from the
woman who first arrived here.'

'You have changed too.'

He did not answer and she focused on the pool again.
She saw his reflection in the limpid water : tall and dark,
his shirt a splash of white. She shivered suddenly and
stepped away from him.

'I must go to the children. In this hot weather they get
restless.'

'There's no need to take your duties so seriously.
You're only a nanny as far as the outside world is concerned. Among the family you're still. . . .'

He paused, discomfited, but she had no wish to help
him and watched as he grew more embarrassed.

'You know what I'm trying to say,' he continued.

She nodded. 'I am not interested in the way your
family regard me.'

'Only the way *I* regard you?'

'Yes. But I am not angry with you for it. I understand
why my coming here has made things difficult for you,
and if I had known the position I would have stayed in
Rovnia. Unfortunately I cannot return there.'

'You mean you would if you could? I thought you
hated the régime?'

'I do. But at least in Rovnia I would be with my own
people. Here, I am a stranger.'

'You'll soon make friends. You are young and beautiful and you will marry again.'

She jerked back sharply. 'What I do with my future is
no concern of yours.'

'It is!'

'Only because you have a guilty conscience.'

'Maybe.' Adrian gnawed at his lower lip. 'I met Mrs
Parkins—who runs the post office—she asked me this
morning about Betty's new nanny. She wondered if you
were a friend of my wife's!'

'What do the people in the village think happened to
your wife?' Tanya asked.

'They know she divorced me.'

'Then you have nothing to worry about.'

'You make it sound so simple. You don't give me credit for having a conscience.'

'What happened to your conscience when I was in Rovnia?'

'Damn it, I tried to get you out, but it was impossible. You still can't see what I went through,' he added. 'I know it's hard for you, but if you could see my point of view....' His brows drew together. 'We've not only matured in the past eight years, we've grown apart; seen different things, lived different lives. When your Embassy told me you'd divorced me I determined to forget you. I told myself it was useless to think about the past when there was so much to be done in the future. I made myself put love behind me and——'

'How can you say that when you're engaged to another woman?' she cried. 'Or are you telling me you don't love her either?'

'What I feel for Diana is different from what I felt for you,' he said sharply. 'She understands politics and she will make me an admirable wife.'

'But do you love her? Do you want her with all your heart?'

Adrian did not reply for so long that Tanya had given up expecting an answer when he suddenly spoke. 'Diana and I have a great deal in common. She isn't a demanding woman either, and she has many interests of her own.'

'If that's the sort of marriage that will make you happy,' Tanya said bitterly, 'then you were a fool ever to have married *me*! I am glad you stopped loving me, Adrian. I see now we would never have been happy together!'

'If you had come to England with me, everything

would have been different. But one can't live on memories, and when you try to pick up the threads of your life again you automatically—without meaning to—weave a different pattern. I know it's hard on you, Tanya, but we must make the best of things.'

'Such sentiments are too British for me! I can't make the best of something I hate. I don't want to go on staying here, Adrian. I want to leave your house—make another life for myself where I won't have to see you.'

'As soon as it's safe for you to go, I'll——'

'Safe for *me*!' she cut in. 'Don't you mean when it's safe for *you*? That's all you're thinking of, Adrian. Yourself!'

Anger brought a rush of colour to his face, taking away his usual pallor and making him look younger. 'I happen to be thinking of all the people who're trying to get me elected to Parliament. If it weren't for my commitment to them, I'd never have asked you to stay here. However, if you find it intolerable, I'll take you to London and put you in a hotel. As I've already told you, you're still my responsibility wherever you are.'

With a murmur she flung up her hands. 'You make it impossible for me to go! If I leave here and you lose the election, I will always blame myself.'

'You weren't to know the position when you came here,' he said heavily. 'But if Roger Poulton found out who you were, he'd use it to harm me.'

'But I hate the Rovnian dictatorship,' she cried. 'Why couldn't you say that?'

'And what about my engagement to Diana? What do you think the newspapers would make of that? A man with a wife *and* a fiancée! That would really go down well with the electorate.'

'Perhaps if you saw Mr Poulton and explained the position...'

'He'd do anything to smear my name,' he told her.

'Is he so wicked?'

'It has nothing to do with being wicked. But we're fighting an election and he'll use every weapon he can lay his hands on to beat me.'

'Would you do the same?'

'No,' Adrian said tersely. 'But then I'm not as committed to politics as Poulton is.'

'Then why do you care so much about winning?'

'Because I have given my word.' Tanya's eyes filled with tears and she remembered another time when he had given his word: when they had stood side by side at the British Embassy and exchanged their marriage vows.

'I wish things could have been different,' he said huskily. 'I've never wanted to hurt you; please believe that.'

Not trusting herself to answer, she ran back to the house.

From then on she was careful to keep out of his way. All there was to say had been said between them; henceforth she must forget the man she had married and look upon Adrian as a stranger.

Everyone in the village now accepted her as nanny to Mrs Tufton's children, and even Mrs Parkins—without whose gossiping tongue Tanya would not have been forced to remain here—accepted her at face value, and said that if Tanya wished to find a better paid job, she would be able to put one her way. But Tanya knew that when she left Adrian's home she would not want to keep in touch with anyone who had known her during her stay here.

She paused in her thoughts and, at the same time, paused in her walking. She had left the children with Betty and was enjoying the unexpected relaxation of being alone. For nearly a week the sky had been overcast, but now the sun had broken through and she had taken advantage of the change in the weather to get herself some exercise. Instead of going for a brisk walk she had automatically made for the woods, as if the shadowy gloom of the evergreens formed a suitable backcloth for her thoughts.

But from now on she would try to think more positively. Her English had improved and with it had come a greater sense of confidence. The shabby little Rovnian refugee had disappeared and the lovely, slender girl with corn-gold hair who had replaced her required no pity or help from anyone.

She turned to retrace her steps and saw a man coming towards her. His red hair flamed in the sun and his eyes were vivid blue in a thin, lined face.

'Lovely day, isn't it?' he said pleasantly.

At his inevitable reference to the weather, a dimple showed in her cheek. She returned his greeting and was about to move past him when he stopped her.

'You're a stranger here, aren't you?' he said. 'Are you on holiday?'

'No. I live at Park Gates. I look after Mrs Tufton's children.'

'Ah yes, I've heard about you. I'm Roger Poulton, by the way.'

Her eyes widened, but she said composedly: 'I'm Tanya Kovacs.' She went to walk on, but he fell into step beside her.

'I take it you know I'm Adrian Chesterton's opponent in the election?' he said.

'I have heard of nothing else since I arrived.'

'I'll bet!' His glance was mischievous. 'Who do you think will win?'

She gave the question serious thought. 'It will be— what you call—a close battle.'

'A close fight,' he corrected. 'Though I'm sure our politics are pretty tame compared with Rovnian ones!'

'In my country we do not have elections any more,' she said bitterly, 'but one day we will be free.'

'I'm sure you will.' His tone was understanding and she warmed towards him, though the feeling evaporated as he said: 'How did you manage to escape? Did Chesterton pull any strings to get you out?'

'I managed,' she said evasively.

'What made you decide to come to England?'

'Because the English don't ask questions!'

'I deserved that!' he smiled. 'But I wasn't being curious. I'm genuinely interested. Please accept my apologies.'

'I will,' she said solemnly. 'But now if you will excuse me, I must return home.'

Thoughtfully Tanya went back to the house. In future she would not go walking in the woods; it would at least ensure she did not meet Roger Poulton again.

But in this Tanya reckoned without fate, for a few days later, as she and the children were looking into the window of the village sweetshop, discussing the rival merits of fruit gums and toffee, she heard his voice behind her.

'I should go for toffees,' he advised. 'They last longer!'

Tanya laughed. 'You hear that, children? You had better do as Mr Poulton says.'

'I want toffees *and* fruit gums,' said Emma.

'You don't have enough money to buy both,' Tanya replied.

'*I* want both,' Tim intervened, and started wailing. 'I want both! I want both!'

Hastily Roger intervened. 'I've a much better idea. Why don't you buy the toffees and then I'll take you to the Copper Kettle for an ice-cream. How about that?'

Immediately appeased, Tim stopped crying. 'Now?' he demanded.

'Now,' Roger agreed, and looked at Tanya. 'You will let me take them, won't you?'

'How can I refuse without having a revolution?'

'There was method in my madness,' he said sotto voce, and looked so pleased with himself that Tanya was hard pressed not to laugh.

Their purchase of toffees completed, the children trotted happily along to the Copper Kettle, and were soon seated at a pseudo-Jacobean table, enjoying their ice-cream.

'I think you understand children,' Tanya murmured to her host.

'I should do. I have three brothers and four sisters.'

'And you all still live together?'

'Two of my sisters have married and left home.'

'Are you married?' she asked.

'I've been too busy. Politics is a full-time occupation.'

'Your family must be proud of you.'

'I like to think so. If I can win this——'

'Tanya!' Tim wailed suddenly. 'I want another ice-cream!'

'No, dear,' said Tanya. 'One is quite enough. And anyway, it is time for us to go. I promised to get some stamps for mother.'

Roger Poulton walked with them to the Post Office, where Emma announced that she would stay with the nice man while Tanya went inside.

'Are you sure you don't mind?' Tanya asked him.

'Being seen with children is good for my image,' he grinned, and ruffled Emma's hair as Tanya and Tim disappeared. 'You're a spoilt little lady,' he said, 'but pretty enough to get away with it.'

'I'm not spoilt. Tanya says I'm very good. She never gets cross with me.'

'I'm glad to hear it.'

'But sometimes she cries,' Emma stated, 'but not 'cos we're naughty. I think she misses her mummy.'

'Then you should be especially nice to her.'

'We are,' said Emma, 'But she still cries.'

Roger was about to comment when Tanya came back, a proud Tim holding aloft a book of stamps which Emma immediately tried to take from him. Once more Roger came to the rescue, though it was several minutes before peace was restored sufficiently for walking to be resumed.

'I feel most guilty for imposing upon you like this,' Tanya apologised.

'I've told you, it's good for votes. Ask Adrian and see if he agrees!'

'I do not talk to Mr Chesterton about the election,' she said stiffly.

Roger's eyebrows rose, but he made no comment. Soon they reached the crossroads and he stopped to say goodbye. 'I'll be delighted to buy you all ice-cream again one afternoon.'

'You must not spoil us,' Tanya protested, and quickly shepherded her two charges away, unaware of Roger watching her, a puzzled expression on his face as they disappeared down the drive that led to Adrian Chesterton's imposing home.

CHAPTER FOUR

SINCE the night of her arrival, Tanya had only glimpsed Adrian's fiancée, and she wondered if the girl was deliberately staying out of her way or was doing so at Adrian's request. She knew they were together frequently, for Diana was helping him with his campaign, but she never dined at the house and her name was rarely mentioned.

It was therefore a surprise to Tanya when she went into the drawing-room one afternoon and found Diana sitting in an armchair by the window.

'I'm s-sorry,' Tanya stammered, and made to withdraw. 'I did not see you.'

'There's no need for you to go,' came the reply. 'I'm waiting for Adrian, and he's sure to be a while yet. Won't you stay and talk to me?'

'I do not think we have anything to say to each other.'

'I don't see why not. We can at least be friendly even if we can't be friends.'

Tanya was amazed. How strange the English were; how coolly they took everything!

'It would be difficult for me to be friendly towards you,' she said, her English more constrained through nervousness. 'You are betrothed to Adrian and I—I am married to him.'

'It does sound rather awful when you put it like that!'

'How else should I put it? All I have said is the truth.'

'I know, but—but it isn't quite the way it sounds, is it?

I mean, you and Adrian are divorced and—and you were both so young when you married.'

'But we *were* married,' Tanya stated harshly, 'and we did love each other.'

'I'm sure you did,' Diana said gently, 'and I know you're in an awful position. But it's equally bad for me. You do see that, surely?'

'I see only that you have no heart.'

'No heart?'

'If you loved Adrian, you could not be polite to me. You would hate me!'

'I have no reason to hate you.'

The calm reply was far more shattering to Tanya's self-esteem than an angry one. The girl was right to feel secure. After all, she knew Adrian as he was today; and the man of today could never have loved a girl like Tanya.

'I don't mean to be rude,' Diana continued, 'but I do think it's silly of both of us not to face facts.'

'You are right,' Tanya said with difficulty. 'You have no reason to be jealous of me. But even so, I think you *would* be if you were truly in love with my—with Adrian.'

'I do love him,' Diana said coolly, 'but I appreciate why he hasn't sent you away. It would be fatal to his career if there were any scandal about him now.'

She stopped as Adrian came in. 'Sorry I'm late, Diana,' he began and stopped short as he saw Tanya. He flushed but otherwise remained composed. 'Hello, Tanya, I didn't know you were here.'

'I am just going,' she replied.

'There's no need to leave on our account. Diana and I are going out.'

Tanya shrugged and went over to a side table, where

she pretended to be absorbed in one of the magazines
that lay there. She heard him say goodbye but did not
look up till they had gone. Then, unable to prevent herself, she stood by the window and watched them walk
down the drive. How cold they were together, she
thought. Did they never kiss or touch each other? Was
their only greeting a casual 'Sorry I'm late'? Surely all
English couples were not like this? Even as the thought
came into her mind she remembered how passionate
Adrian had once been. He couldn't have changed so
much. There must be a reason for his present attitude.

As though conscious that Tanya was watching them,
Diana suddenly took hold of Adrian's arm and moved
close to him. At the sight of them linked together, Tanya
felt such a pang of jealousy that it was like a physical
pain. Blindly she turned away and buried her face in her
hands. And she had thought she was getting over her
love for him! How wrong she was. She loved him today
as much as she had ever done.

Knowing that if she remained alone she would give
way to tears, she ran up to the nursery where Betty had
just finished bathing the children. Flushed and damp-
looking in their blue dressing-gowns, they sat on the
hearthrug while she read a story to them.

'Have you also come to hear *The Adventures of
Twizzle*?' Betty grinned.

'I always like to hear about him,' Tanya smiled back.
'I know the stories by heart.'

'So do these monsters of mine, but they still insist I
read it to them.'

'Children enjoy the security of repetition.'

'Adults like security too,' said Betty, then seeing the
shattered look on Tanya's face, was immediately contrite. 'You look as if you need cheering up.'

'That is why I have come to hear a *Twizzle* story.'

A knock on the door prevented Betty from replying. It was Jean, their daily help, to say that Tanya was wanted on the telephone.

'Are you sure it is for me?' Tanya questioned. 'I do not know anyone who would call me.'

'It's a gentleman, miss, but he didn't give his name.'

Puzzled, Tanya ran downstairs. Was it someone from the Rovnian Embassy trying to pressurise her into returning to her own country? But her parents were dead and they no longer had any pressure they could bring to bear. Nonetheless her hands were damp as she lifted the receiver and said, 'Hello.'

'Hello yourself,' Roger Poulton replied. 'I was beginning to think you were leaving me hanging!'

'I was with the children,' she said breathlessly.

'How about being with me instead? For dinner tonight. I realise it's short notice, but I didn't know I'd be free until now. I can pick you up in an hour.'

'An hour?' she echoed, not sure what to do.

'That's right. I thought we'd go to the Merry Dragon. The food's good there and they have dancing. You do dance, don't you?'

Still Tanya hesitated. Was it right for her to go out with another man while she was still Adrian's wife? The very thought of Adrian gave her the impetus to say yes, and having agreed to be ready in an hour, she ran to tell Betty.

'Are you sure it's wise?' queried Betty. 'After all, he *is* Adrian's opponent.'

'Does that make him his enemy?'

'Of course not. As children they used to play together. But the by-election they're fighting isn't a game and— well, Adrian mightn't like it.'

'There are many things Adrian has done that *I* do not like,' Tanya retorted, and knew from Betty's chastened expression that she had put an end to the conversation.

But while she was changing to go out, Tanya's conscience reasserted itself and, had she known where to contact Roger, she would have changed her mind.

Nervously she went down to the hall and opened the front door, anxious to be there when he arrived. In that way she might prevent him from ringing the door bell and might, with luck, prevent the rest of the family from discovering with whom she was going out. Yet what did it matter if Adrian minded or not? He didn't care whether she herself objected to his seeing Diana! But she knew the two things could not be equated and her conscience was still pricking her when a small dark saloon drew to a stop on the gravel driveway, and she went down the steps to greet Roger.

In a dark suit, and with his red hair slicked back from his forehead instead of falling untidily over it, he looked unfamiliar, and for a brief instant she felt a pang of uneasiness. This man was a stranger. To have an ice-cream with him when she was with the children was one thing, but to spend an entire evening in his company was something different. But then everything was turning out to be different from what she had expected. She sighed and made herself more comfortable in the car.

'I'm sorry I had to give you such short notice,' he said with a swift glance in her direction. 'But I'm awfully pleased you could make it.'

'I do not have a diary full of engagements.'

'I'm sure you could have. You're a lovely-looking young woman.'

She was warmed by the compliment. 'I have improved much in the last few months.'

'How can you improve on perfection?' Roger asked.

'All women are improved by beautiful clothes and the right kind of make-up.'

'Meaning you don't get them in Rovnia?'

'There are many things we don't get there. But freedom is the biggest thing we lack.'

'That's why so many Rovnians have escaped. There's quite a contingent in London, you know.'

'No—I didn't. But I'm not sure I—I do not think I would like to get in touch with them.'

'Why not?'

Tanya was silent, regretting what she had said. It was quite feasibly that some of her compatriots would know she was Professor Kovacs' daughter, and would also remember she had once been married to a British diplomat. From there it was but a short step to remembering his name—particularly if it was seen in the national newspapers. Yet she dared not say this to Roger and she sought for a way of parrying his curiosity.

'It is not good for refugees to be with other refugees. If one is continually associated with the past, one tends to hanker for it.'

'Even though you hated it?'

'I do not hate my country,' she said with dignity. 'Only its present rulers.'

'Of course.' He looked contrite. 'It was a silly thing for me to say. I apologise.'

'I accept it.'

He laughed.

'Have I said something wrong?'

'Not at all. But you sounded quaint.'

He slowed down as they approached a roundabout, then headed for the main London road. Soon the Merry Dragon came into sight. It was a modern clubhouse set in its own grounds, and despite the early hour there were already many cars parked alongside it.

Expecting loud music and garish decor, Tanya was surprised by the almost sombre furnishings and the quiet, elegantly dressed people whom she glimpsed going into the restaurant.

'How about a drink at the bar first?' Roger suggested.

'I am not a drinker,' she apologised. 'One glass of wine and I am on the table!'

'Under it,' he corrected with a smile, and steered her towards the dining-room.

They were shown to a corner table sufficiently clear of the band to enable them to talk without having to shout, yet near enough to the dance floor to watch the couples. Overwhelmed by the vast menu, Tanya begged Roger to choose her meal for her, which he did after first ascertaining that she preferred soup to hors d'oeuvres and meat to fish.

'I'll leave you to choose the sweet for yourself,' he said when the waiter had taken their order.

'If I'm not too full, I'll have something with cream.'

'You sound just like Emma!'

'Sometimes I feel like a child,' she admitted, 'but at other times. . . .'

'Don't!' He leaned over and caught her hand. It was the second time he had done so this evening and she found his clasp strangely comforting.

'Don't what?' she asked.

'Don't get that sad look on your face. I can always tell when you're thinking of the past; and you shouldn't, you know. You should think only of the future.'

'Sometimes the future is sad too.'

'Yours won't be. You're young enough to make it what you want.'

'That is not always possible.' She looked at him with

curiosity. 'What will you do if you lose the election?'

'I won't lose it.'

She was stung by his complacency. 'Adrian is a clever man too. He may beat you.'

'I doubt it.' Brown eyes regarded her. 'Do you call him Adrian to his face?'

She was startled by the question. 'Of course not. Why do you ask?'

'Because his name came so easily to you that I wondered——'

'Then do not wonder,' she said sharply. 'The children talk of him often and I am used to hearing his name.'

She was relieved to see the waiter approaching with their first course, and determinedly changed the conversation. But when she was tackling the succulent steak Roger had ordered for her, he referred to Adrian again, doing it so naturally that she had no cause for suspicion.

'Even when we were children,' he said, 'I always knew we'd end up on opposing sides—with me fighting for the underdog and Adrian championing big business.'

'He fights for the underdog too,' said Tanya. 'He cares about the farmers and agricultural workers as much as you do.'

'You sound as if Adrian's been preaching at you!'

'He is too busy to concern himself with his sister's nanny,' she said composedly.

'God, what a snob you make him sound!'

'Then I am giving you the wrong impression. All I meant is that—is that to him I am just someone in the house.'

'Like a doormat.'

'Why do you dislike him?' she asked curiously.

'Why do you defend him?' Roger countered. 'Did you know him before you came here?'

'What a silly question! How could I?'

'I don't know. It's something Emma said.'

'Emma! Have you been trying to get information from a child?' Tanya was so angry she could not stop her voice rising, and Roger looked at her in surprise.

'Of course I haven't. But when I was waiting for you outside the Post Office she said something that gave me the impression you'd known him in the past. He was stationed in Rovnia at one time.'

'Many years ago.' Tanya was aware of her lips trembling and compressed them tightly.

'Not all that long. Eight or nine years.'

'I was a child then. Only eighteen.'

'So young! You're so sedate I keep thinking of you as being older than you are.'

'That is a bad compliment!'

'I meant it to be a nice one,' he said swiftly, and paused as if searching for the right word. 'You're serene,' he said finally. 'I can't imagine you ever being a rumbustious teenager.'

'I never was,' she admitted. 'I grew up in a serious-minded household.'

'Then it's time you stopped being serious. You're in a new country and you must learn to enjoy life.' He pushed back his chair. 'I suggest we start now.'

'Here?' she asked, startled.

'By taking the floor and dancing.'

'I have forgotten how. It is so long since I danced.'

'I'll teach you.'

Made confident by the unaccustomed wine she had drunk, Tanya suddenly felt herself in a carefree mood and, clasped in Roger's arms, gave herself up to the music. He was a surprisingly good dancer and as he felt her gain confidence, his steps became more intricate.

'You're doing splendidly,' he said.

'Only because of you.' She tilted her face and laughed

up at him, the sound dying in her throat as the movement of her head brought the table behind Roger into
her line of vision. Adrian and Diana were seated there,
and though the girl gave a faint inclination of her head,
Adrian stared at her icily.

'What's wrong?' Roger asked.

'Adrian's here. With Diana.'

'So what? There's no law against your coming out
with me.' Despite his casual tone, Roger also seemed to
lose colour, though it could have been a trick of the light.

As if by mutual consent they returned to their table.
Their plates had been cleared away and he beckoned to
the waiter to bring the sweet trolley. Afraid that if she
allowed him to begin the conversation, he would once
again refer to Adrian, Tanya said the first thing that
came into her head.

'Do you know Diana Biddell too?' she asked.

'Sure. We played together as kids. Have you ever
heard of Little Lord Fauntleroy?'

'Yes,' she said, puzzled, 'but what has that to do
with——'

'Well, Diana was Little *Lady* Fauntleroy. She had a
governess, but sometimes she'd give her the slip and
come round to my house. My God, that must have been
slumming for her!'

'You make it sound as if you do not see her any
more?'

'I don't. Haven't done for years. I won a scholarship
to university and she went off to finishing school. We
rarely met after that.' He crumpled his napkin. 'When
are they getting married?'

'I don't know.' Tanya fumbled for her compact and
made a pretence of powdering her face. 'I would like to
go home, Roger. I have a headache.'

'Don't let those two send you away,' he said roughly.

'It has nothing to do with them. My headache is real.'

At once he signalled for their bill, then holding her lightly by the arm he led her to the exit. They had to pass Adrian's table and he half-rose from his seat as they did so, though Diana gave Tanya such an unexpected look of dislike that she was startled.

'She does not like to see us together.' she murmured as they drove away from the roadhouse.

'Perhaps she doesn't think it right for a nanny to dine in the same place as herself,' Roger remarked.

'I'm sure that isn't the reason.'

'Then maybe she's jealous in case Adrian fancies you.'

'Don't say that!' Angrily Tanya swung round in her seat.

'Why not? You're beautiful and Adrian's a man.'

'He's also engaged to Diana.'

Roger looked rueful. 'You're right. You always are. Forget what I said, will you?'

She nodded, but remained tense until they drew to a stop outside Park Gates. Ignoring her protest that he should not get out of the car, Roger came round to open the door for her, then walked with her to the front door.

'Will you let me see you again, Tanya?'

'Only if we don't talk about——'

'Adrian?' he finished for her. 'I give you my promise.'

'Then I will see you again.'

Swiftly she went into the house, pausing in the hall until she heard him drive away. Only then did she slip through the drawing-room and into the garden. She was too overwrought to sleep and made her way to her favourite spot by the lily pond. The moon made phosphorescent ripples on the surface and outlined the pale lilies with silver. How lovely it was here! How peaceful. If only her life was the same. For a long while she remained by the water, then finally returned to the house, knowing that true peace would never be hers until she left Park Gates.

It was only as she went into the hall that she noticed a light shining under the library door and guessed Adrian was home. Her heart began to pound and keeping her steps light, she hurried to the stairs. But as her foot reached the bottom step the library door opened, and she heard him call her name.

Slowly she turned. He was framed in the doorway, looking as composed as he always did. Yet not quite. As he moved forward a step she saw that his hair was ruffled, as if he had disturbed it with his hands. His expression too was disturbed: the muscles taut at the sides of his mouth, his jaw looking more aggressive because of it.

'Come into the library, please. I want to talk to you.'

Nervously she walked past him into the library. He closed the door, then leant against it, staring at her in a silence that seemed interminable. But she stood her ground and stared back at him, determined not to speak first.

'How long have you known Roger Poulton?' he asked finally.

'A couple of weeks.'

'Have you been out with him before?'

'I've met him a few times with the children, but to-night was the first time I've been out with him alone.'

'Have you forgotten who he is?'

'No.'

'Then why the hell did you go out with him? You know damn well he's my opponent.'

The strength of his anger gave her a momentary elation, before quickly fading as she reminded herself he was only angry because Roger was his political rival. It had nothing to do with his emotions.

'Why shouldn't I go out with him?' she asked. 'I'm living here as your sister's nanny, and what I do in my free time has nothing to do with you.'

'You were once my wife,' he said curtly. 'Technically you still are. If that doesn't mean anything to you. . . .'

'To me?' she cried in astonishment. 'I'm the one who came to England to find you. *You* were the one who turned me away.'

'I didn't turn you away.'

'You are not being honest with your words,' she cried. 'If it hadn't been for your all-important election you'd have sent me away immediately. But instead you begged me to stay. You never stopped to consider how *I* would feel about it. All that mattered to you was your career.'

'I didn't realise that staying in my home was such a hardship for you,' he said quietly.

'Then you're a fool!' Wildly she rushed to the door, knowing that if she stayed here any longer she would say something she would regret. But as her fingers fumbled on the handle, Adrian twisted her round to face him.

'You can't go like this. I didn't mean to hurt you—I never have. But neither of us are to blame for what has happened.'

'I do not blame you for the past.' Tears poured down her cheeks. 'Only for the way you behave now. I want to get out of your life. I want to build my *own* future.'

Her voice choked and she was unable to continue. Her tears flowed faster and she put her hands to her eyes. It was a childlike gesture that seemed to be his undoing, for with a murmur he pulled her into his arms and stroked her hair.

'Don't cry, Tanya. Please don't cry.'

His voice was the gentle one she remembered in her dreams; the voice that had whispered words of love when they had lain together and sworn never to kiss, never to touch, never to belong to anyone else. She knew she should pull away from him, that to stay close was to warm herself against a fire that could burn into her soul. But she did not have the will-power to move. She was being held by the man she loved and, if nothing else, it would give her a newer memory to cherish.

'I wish things had been different,' he said thickly. 'I've tried to forget the past—it was the only way I could go on—but since you came back into my life. . . .'

Trembling, he began to kiss her. His lips were firm, but as they touched hers, they seemed to melt and fuse upon her. There was no strangeness in his hold, no strangeness in the smell of him or the murmuring voice that whispered her name over and over, as if it were a benediction. The years of their separation dissolved as though they had never been and remembered response was fired by remembered response as mounting passion drew them close.

His hands moved down her back to clasp her close and pull her body hard against the hardness of his. 'Tanya ... I want you.'

His words found an echo in her heart and her hands cradled his neck, her fingers twining themselves in his silky brown hair. It was as if they had made love to one another every night, so instantaneous was their mutual need. His mouth knew how to arouse her; his hands knew where to explore, and though she tried to hold herself aloof from him, a deep familiar languor was pervading her limbs.

From the time Adrian had kissed her goodbye at the airport eight years ago, Tanya had allowed no man to touch her. Night after night she had lain in her virginal bed, where she had lain as a child, and remembered the brief rhapsody of her marriage, knowing that until she was reunited with the man she loved, she would remain alone. As the years passed, she had wondered what her reactions would be when she was finally with him again, and had often been afraid that desire, for so long dormant, would take time to be reawakened.

But no time had been needed. The moment she had felt Adrian's body she had wanted him to invade her; had known that without him she was a clock without hands, a waterfall without water, a sea without a shore. Yet Adrian could never be her shore. In his arms she could find no harbour in which to rest. He belonged to another woman and to let him go on holding her was to usurp that other woman's place. The gall of rejection soured her desire, eating away the delicate tissue of love and giving her the strength to push him away.

'How *can* you?' she cried. 'I'm not a doll you can pick up and kiss whenever the fancy takes you! I'm a woman, Adrian, and I want love, not lust. If you're so desperate to be satisfied, you should go to Diana!'

'Tanya, I——'

Without waiting to hear more, she rushed from the room. Only when she reached the top of the stairs did she pause and glance back. But if she had expected to see Adrian coming after her, she was disappointed, for the hall was in darkness and the door of the library was closed. He had listened to her words and had taken them to heart. It was a good thing he had been unable to hear her heart itself, for if he had, they would not be apart now. But this was the way it had to be, and to pretend otherwise was to live in a fool's paradise.

CHAPTER FIVE

For a long while after Tanya had run from the room, Adrian remained there bereft of all feeling. But gradually emotion returned; not the desire which had caused him to lose his self-control but a deep sense of shame that he should have behaved the way he had done.

No wonder Tanya had been angry. But it was nothing to the anger he felt towards himself. For an instant he debated whether to go after her and make some kind of apology, but then decided against it. They were both in too emotional a state for him to run the risk of igniting the passion that had flared so dangerously between them.

He went round the side of his desk and sat down at his chair. For the first time in years he did not feel in command of himself. It was an unfamiliar feeling, and he did not like it. But then there was a great deal he did not like about the situation he was in; a great deal he did not like about himself. That was the crux of it. It was his own behaviour which he found so unsavoury.

Yet when he had asked Tanya to remain here it had not seemed so wrong. It was only now—seeing his request through her eyes—that he realised that to expect a woman who loved him—who had travelled halfway across Europe in search of him—to remain in his home when she knew he was going to marry someone else had been the height of cruelty.

Was he so ambitious to further his career that he could ride roughshod over other people's feelings? He had never used to be that way. The young man who had

married Tanya would never have put business achieve-
ment before personal contentment. But then, once he
had left Rovnia, he had not known contentment for a
long time. It had only been in the past six months that
he had again come near to finding a sense of peace. But
it was a peace which Tanya's arrival had shattered. A
peace that would not be restored even after she had
gone.

Yes, that was the unpalatable truth and he might as
well face it. Even when Tanya left here, he would never
forget her. With an angry mutter he pushed back his
chair and went to stand at the window. The lawns were
drenched in moonlight and the muted colour of the landscape helped to dim the painful vividness of his
thoughts. If only he could put back the clock! But how
far would he want to push it? To the time when Tanya
had first come here or to the time when he had first met
her? And did he wish that they had never met? Remembering her sweetness, the pliant young body that
had responded so ardently to him, he knew the answer to
that.

He banged his clenched fist on the window ledge. The
sound disturbed some birds nesting in the creepers that
clung to the grey stone walls outside, and there was a
soft twitter, almost of disapproval. With a sigh he moved
away from the window. Because he could not find peace
for himself, it did not give him the right to disturb the
peace of other creatures. Musing on the whimsicality of
his thoughts, he switched off the light and went to his
room.

But here there was no peace either, for it was all too
easy to envisage Tanya sleeping a few yards away from
him, her long hair unwound from its confining coil and
spread around her like a golden cobweb. How he had

loved to twine the strands around his body; to ensnare himself visibly as he had begun to ensnare her physically. Yes, they had both been prisoners of their love, never believing there would come a time when they would want to escape. But Tanya hadn't wanted to escape. Through the years of their separation she had gone on loving him. The knowledge had made him hate himself for letting her down, yet tonight—when he had seen her with Roger and should have been pleased that she was making other friends—he had found himself gripped with jealousy. Yet how could he be jealous of one woman when he had pledged himself to another? Was man so possessive that he always wanted to retain what he had once had? It was a disquieting thought, but it had to be faced. He tried to think of Tanya objectively, but found it impossible; the girl of the past and the girl of the present had blurred into one image.

Restlessly he switched on his light. It was better to read than to try and court sleep that would not come, or to remain in the darkness with thoughts that were better left in his subconscious. Right now he had a political fight on his hands and must give it all his energies. There would be time to think of his personal life when victory was his. Victory—what a hollow word it was! With another sigh he concentrated firmly on the text in front of him.

For the rest of the week Adrian and Tanya did their best to avoid each other. She continued to have her meals in the nursery and only came down to the dining-rom for Sunday lunch. No reference was made to Roger and it was not until she inadvertently bumped into Diana, who had come over to tea, that the subject was mentioned.

'I've been wanting a chance to talk to you,' Diana

said, coming towards her across the hall. 'It's about Roger Poulton.'

'I do not wish to discuss him,' Tanya replied. 'He is my friend and I have every intention of seeing him! Nor do I believe that he will harm Adrian.'

'Of course he won't harm Adrian,' Diana stated. 'But it isn't Adrian I'm thinking of. It's you.'

'Me?'

'Yes. Roger could hurt you. All he's concerned with is getting to the top as fast as he can. He isn't interested in anything else.'

'Like Adrian.'

'Not at all like Adrian. There's a world of difference between them. If you can't see that for yourself, there's no point talking about it!'

Heels clicked sharply across the parquet floor, the library door slammed and once again Tanya was alone. Puzzled, she went to her room. Diana had no reason to like her and no reason to mind whether or not Roger hurt her. That being the case, why should she concern herself about their friendship?

It was a question that remained with her for the rest of the afternoon, and only when she went in search of the children at teatime was she able to put it into the back of her mind.

'I thought I told you to have the rest of the day off,' Betty said as Tanya came into the nursery.

'I enjoy being with the children,' Tanya smiled. 'It gives me something to do.'

'Me too. I get bored doing nothing.'

'You should be running your own home.' Tanya put her hand to her mouth, dismayed by her frankness. 'Forgive me, I had no right to say that.'

'It's true,' Betty admitted.

'But you do not like keeping house.'

'What makes you say that? Because I don't do it?' Betty looked whimsical. 'Mother would have a fit if I did anything around here. She'd say I was usurping the staff's position.'

'Then move,' said Tanya, 'and have your own position.'

'That's what Dick says. But I've got into a rut here and have let things slide. You should keep nagging me, then I might do something about it.'

'I do not like to nag you,' Tanya said seriously.

'I don't see why not. You're the nearest thing to a sister I've ever had and——' Betty stopped dismayed as she saw Tanya's eyes fill with tears. 'Oh, lord, I didn't mean to make you cry!'

'I'm not crying because I'm sad.' Tanya fumbled for her handkerchief and pressed it to her eyes. 'But it's the nicest thing anyone has said to me since I came to England.'

Betty put an arm round Tanya's shoulders, glancing quickly at Emma and Tim who were watching the scene wide-eyed.

'Let's go into the other room a minute, Tanya. The kids can play by themselves.'

Gratefully Tanya went into the night nursery and perched on Emma's bed while Betty leaned against the side of it and watched her.

'You weren't really crying because of what I said. Something else has upset you, hasn't it?'

'In a way. I'm being silly about it, but. . . .'

'Is it to do with Roger Poulton?'

Tanya nodded. 'Everyone says it is wrong for me to go on seeing him.'

'*I* haven't said so.'

'But you think it?'

'No, I don't,' said Betty. 'You'd never tell Roger anything that might harm Adrian, nor would Roger expect you to. Personally, I think you're at liberty to go out with him every night of the week if that's what you wish. Don't let my family sit on you, Tanya. We can be a domineering lot if we're given the chance!'

'I still feel I'm being disloyal,' Tanya confessed. 'If Adrian had not—not lost his temper when he spoke to me about Roger, I would have agreed to do as he wished.'

'Thank goodness you didn't. He's far too used to getting his own way. You're only his wife because of a legal technicality, you know. You should remember that.' Seeing surprise in the violet eyes, Betty shrugged. 'I'm not being a disloyal sister. I'm trying to be honest.'

'You are very good and kind.' In an unusual burst of emotion Tanya jumped up and kissed Betty on the cheek, then stepped back quickly as she saw the English girl blush. 'Now I will bath the children and leave you to read them their bedtime story.'

'Only if you promise to come to the cinema with Dick and myself this evening. I'm not having you moping around any longer.'

Tanya nodded and turned to swallow the lump in her throat. Since her last quarrel with Adrian her emotions were raw, and anger—or kindness—could equally be her undoing.

'I would like that,' she said huskily. 'It helps to improve my English.'

She was in her bedroom changing when there was a call from Roger. Reluctant to take it in the hall in case she should see Adrian, she went into Betty's private apartment.

'You sound miles away,' Roger commented as her voice came over the line.

'Because I am speaking on one of the extensions.'

'Then we'll make it short and sweet,' he said. 'Are you free to have dinner with my family tomorrow night?'

'I do not know your family,' she panicked. 'And they are such a large one—they will make me shy!'

Roger chuckled. 'You won't be shy once you meet them. I promise you that!'

'Then I will be happy to come. But don't bother to collect me. I will enjoy a walk to the village.'

There was a pause and she knew he did not believe her.

'Very well,' he murmured. 'But if it's raining and you want a lift, call me.'

Luckily the following evening was a fine one and Tanya walked happily to the village and met Roger strolling through the High Street to meet her. With some trepidation she entered his home, a small semi-detached house set in a large garden which seemed to be full of vegetables.

'My mother's answer to inflation!' Roger grinned, seeing her eye an outsize cauliflower before he pushed her down a narrow hall and into a dining-room that seemed to be full of people. They soon resolved themselves into brothers, sisters and brothers-in-law, all presided over by a buxom and exuberantly friendly Mrs Poulton, who sat at the head of the table dispensing food and dry humour with equal abundance.

'Have some more stew, Tanya?' she said, ladling another portion of succulent meat on to Tanya's plate. 'You look as if you could do with feeding. Do they give you enough to eat up there?'

'More than enough,' Tanya assured her. 'But this is

really delicious. And I have always heard that English
cooking is bad.'

'I think tinned food's nicer than fresh!' piped up
twelve-year-old Brian, the youngest member of the family who, she had learned from Roger, had been born six
months after his father died. 'When you make food
yourself, it tastes different every time, if it's tinned, it
always tastes the same.'

'The same sort of rubbish,' Roger said sarcastically,
and raised his eyebrows at Tanya in mock despair.
'Have you ever met such a frightful brat?'

She smiled. 'Tim and Emma think the same. They too
only like to eat the most horrible things!'

There was general laughter, then one of Roger's sisters
began to ask her about her charges and whether she
liked her job.

Tanya was guarded in her replies and was relieved
when Roger cut the questions to announce that he was
speaking at a meeting in Tipton and was going to take
Tanya with him.

'You and your election!' his mother said. 'I'm sure
Tanya would be much happier sitting here gossiping
with us. Listening to you will bore her stiff.'

Tanya was astounded that Mrs Poulton should speak
in such a way. Adrian's mother treated the election as if
it was something sacred. But then the entire Poulton
family were different from the Chestertons, for where
Adrian was deferred to, Roger was continually teased.

'I would like to go with Roger,' she assured Mrs
Poulton. 'I have never heard him speak.'

There was a burst of laughter round the table. 'You
must have struck him dumb, then,' commented Lydia,
Roger's youngest sister. 'We find it impossible to stop
him speaking!'

Roger grinned as he rose and Tanya obediently followed him to the car, waving goodbye to the family who crowded the garden path to see them off. 'You have a wonderful family,' she said warmly as they drove away.

'They're not bad,' he replied, and Tanya marvelled at the lack of emotion displayed by her new compatriots. It was obvious that a deep affection existed between all the Poultons, yet to praise them to each other elicited only the most casual response. She sighed and wondered if she would ever get used to living in England.

She wondered about this again as she sat in the village hall listening to Roger speak. Some of the audience did not agree with him and continually interrupted him, but the rest of the people took the hecklers in good part, and when the meeting was over quite a few of them joined forces and marched off to the nearest pub.

'That could never happen in my country,' she commented. 'People who are on different sides politically are on different sides in everything.'

'It's becoming a bit like that here too,' Roger said. 'Though mostly in the cities.'

'If you win this election, you will be part of a big city.'

'Do you want me to win?' he asked with a smile.

'You deserve to win,' she said quickly. 'Your speech was excellent.'

But that night as she lay in bed, she knew that however much she liked Roger and his family, she did not want him to win. A few yards away, physically separated by four walls yet mentally separated by so much more, was the one man whom she desperately wanted to succeed: Adrian, her husband.

Did he still fall asleep with one arm above his head? During their brief week of marriage the other arm had lain heavily across her, as if even in sleep he had been afraid she would leave him. Yet he had been the one to leave her, she thought bitterly, and even when she had come to him, he had not wanted her. But no, that wasn't true. He did want her. The way he had kissed her had told her that. But wanting was not loving and she had no regrets at turning him away. All she regretted was that she had ever responded to him, for it had awakened all her dormant desires and now they burned continually within her; no longer were they damped-down fires but glowing embers ready to flame into life at his touch. Yes, it would take only the merest touch from Adrian to set her alight for him; to make her plead for his kisses; to urge him to assuage the deep yearning she felt for him.

My love! she cried silently. My one and only love!

CHAPTER SIX

THE afternoon following Tanya's visit to his home, Roger returned to it tired and dispirited. He had held a meeting in part of the town inhabited by Adrian Chesterton's supporters, and they had hardly let a word of his pass without heckling him. Had Tanya been there, she would not have thought it so different from Rovnian politics after all!

Flinging his hat at the hallstand, he strode towards the sitting-room, pausing as he heard voices there. He recognised one of them as his mother's, but the other was unfamiliar and he straightened his tie. Then he opened the door and went in, stopping abruptly as he saw the slim dark-haired girl on the sofa. What in heaven's name was Diana Biddell doing here?

'Good evening,' he said coldly. 'Did you want to see me?'

'Hello, Roger.' Her voice was calm. 'How are you?'

'Very well, thank you. And the weather's fine too.'

Momentarily Diana looked discomfited and Mrs Poulton stood up.

'I'll leave you two to get on with it while I finish my ironing.'

'There's no need to leave us,' Roger said shortly, glancing from Diana's Gucci shoes and St. Laurent dress to his mother's cotton overall. 'Whatever Miss Biddell wants to say to me can be said in front of you.'

'Maybe so.' Mrs Poulton went to the door. 'But my ironing won't disappear of its own accord!'

Roger compressed his lips and remained silent until the door closed. 'Well, well,' he said heavily. 'It's a long time since you honoured us with a visit. When you were about fifteen, wasn't it? Before your prejudices began to show.'

'My not coming here had nothing to do with prejudice. I was away at finishing school and you were at university. We couldn't expect to see so much of each other.'

'There were still the holidays,' he said tonelessly. 'You could have seen me if you'd wanted. Not that I blame you because you didn't. The plebeian Poultons were never on your father's visiting list!'

'I'd rather we didn't discuss my father,' she said stiffly.

'That would be a pleasure!' Roger stuffed his hands into his pockets. 'What did you come here for?'

She hesitated and he saw her fingers were nervously intertwined. 'I—er—it's about Tanya.' She paused, as if hoping he would say something, but he went on looking at her implacably. 'You're not making it easy for me, are you?'

'Too many people have made it easy for you,' he replied. 'Go on with what you were saying.'

'As I've just told you—it's about Tanya. I don't know what you hope to gain by seeing her.'

For a moment Roger was at a loss for words, then he found them, and his anger with it. 'What does any man hope to gain by seeing a beautiful woman? I'm not in your class socially, Miss Biddell, but physically there's no difference between me and your upper-crust fiancé!'

'You're deliberately misunderstanding me,' Diana said icily. 'You know very well that Tanya is living in Adrian's home and can't help being caught up in his affairs. And since he happens to be your opponent in the election, I should have thought the implication was obvious.'

'The implication being that I'm seeing Tanya for devious reasons?' Roger spoke softly, but anyone who knew him well would have been warned by the pale line that had appeared around his mouth. 'I've no doubt that's the way people in your circle might act, but we workers happen to have a little more self-respect!'

'Must you keep talking like a Marxist student!' Diana burst out. 'Can't you at least be civil to me while I'm here?'

'I could say the same to you! What the hell business do you have coming here and insulting me?'

She bit her lip. 'I'm sorry if you think I have. But I was hoping you would make Tanya see she's doing herself a disservice. If it were after the election it wouldn't matter.'

'It doesn't matter now. You're behaving as if she's got hold of State secrets! All she does is work for Chesterton's sister. And if she wants to go out with me in her free time....'

'I should have known I was wasting my time coming here to talk to you. You're so blinded with prejudice you aren't able to see anyone else's point of view.'

Angrily Diana walked past him, her eyes wide and unblinking, as if moving the lids might precipitate a shower of tears. Roger muttered something and half raised his hand. His fingers brushed her shoulder and she jerked back as though his hand was a flame.

'Afraid of me besmirching you?' he sneered.

'Must you misunderstand everything about me?' she whispered. 'I don't regard you as my enemy, Roger. I never did.'

'You don't regard me as your friend either.'

'I used to.'

'When we were children,' he said. 'Which we can never be again.' On an impulse he bent his head and pressed his mouth on hers.

For a split second she stood motionless, too surprised to resist, then she stepped away from him and glared at him. 'What was that for?'

'To remind you how susceptible I am to beautiful women!' His voice was mocking. 'Aren't you going to slap my face?'

'You've been reading too many cheap novels,' she replied. 'Which really doesn't surprise me.'

Before he could think of a suitable retort she had gone, and he raked his hands through his hair and then went into the kitchen where his mother was still ironing.

'Diana gone?' At his nod she shrugged. 'Pity, I was going to make some tea. Never mind, *we'll* have some instead. Turn off the light under the kettle, Roger, there's a good lad.'

'I doubt if she'd have had tea at this hour of the day,' Roger said, obeying his mother's request. 'She has it at four, with cucumber sandwiches!'

'I'm sure she'd have enjoyed a cup at five-thirty.' Mrs Poulton's tone was as placid as if she were talking to young Brian. 'She's a nice girl, is Diana; as you'd see for yourself if you weren't so obsessed with her father. It's not her fault he's a rich old fool.'

'It's her fault she's a rich *young* fool!' Roger snorted. 'She does nothing with her life.'

'She's a devoted daughter,' Mrs Poulton said, 'and with the father she has, that can't be easy.'

'Do you mind if we don't continue this conversation? I've a meeting tonight and I'd rather like to change into that shirt you're still ironing.'

Mrs Poulton pulled it off the ironing board and slapped it into his hand. 'When you're standing in front of the mirror putting it on,' she said, 'take a good look at yourself at the same time. You mightn't like what you see!' Leaving an astonished man staring after her ample back, she marched out of the kitchen.

Though Roger did not tell Tanya that Diana had been to see him, it make him feel constrained with her, and he found himself wondering if Tanya also assumed he was seeing her for any underhand motives. In order to set the record straight, he mentioned it to her.

She heard him out in silence, her beautiful violet eyes watching him with an innocence that reminded him of a child. Yet she was in no way a child; there was a maturity about her that occasionally astounded him; an ability to get to the heart of a problem: to see facts without emotionalism. In her own way, she had been extremely helpful to him, acting as a sounding board for many of his ideas. It was odd that he talked to her so frankly and openly and it gave him pause for reflection. Though Diana thought that he was seeing Tanya in order to find out what Adrian was doing, he himself had never suspected that Tanya might be seeing him in order to spy for Adrian!

'Our friendship is causing many people to talk,' Tanya said, cutting across his thoughts. 'But it is *my* conscience that concerns me—not other people's.'

'But other people can make things difficult for you,' he said gravely.

'With you as my friend, I can face the difficulty.'

'You speak as if I'm your only friend.' He looked at her curiously. 'What about the Chestertons? I mean, you came straight here to them, didn't you? You must have known them before.'

It was a long time since he had shown curiosity about her working at Park Gates, and Tanya was now prepared for it. 'Betty had her name down with one of the refugee agencies,' she said steadily, 'and I liked the idea of working in the country until I had decided exactly what I wanted to do with my life.'

'You won't spend it being nanny to other women's children,' he said positively. 'You'll marry and have your own.'

'I will never marry again.'

'Again?' He caught her up on the word. 'Have you been married before?'

Shock closed her throat, but she was swift to recover. 'It was just—how you say—a figure of speech.'

'Then if you've never been married,' he smiled, 'how come you're so anti-marriage?'

'I have seen too many unhappy ones.'

'You'll change your mind when you meet the right man.'

She laughed. 'You sound like your mother!'

'Don't tell me she's been having the same conversation with you?' he said ruefully.

'The other day she was trying to make me see how wonderful you are!' Roger looked so discomfited that Tanya laughed. 'Do not worry about it. I was able to make her see we are only friends.'

He was silent for some considerable time before speaking. 'You must think me an odd character. You're beautiful and desirable, yet I haven't tried to make love to you. It isn't that I haven't wanted to. It's just that I don't want to spoil what we have and I think that—that promiscuity might.... Oh hell! I sound like something out of the Ark!'

'You sound like a sincere and charming man,' she said

seriously. 'Having your friendship is far more important to me than having your kisses.'

'One day you will have both from a man,' he said. 'Friendship and love.'

'One day you will have that from a woman.'

'No.' The sound was positive. 'I've years of work ahead of me. If I don't win this election I'll find another seat to fight. I'll be too busy to think of marriage for years.'

Tanya remembered this as she watched the children playing in the garden the following day. It seemed unnatural that someone as intense as Roger should be content to lead a celibate life. Intuitively she felt he was in love with someone or that he had been in the past. Sufficiently in love for it to have soured him too much to consider having a similar relationship with anyone else.

Her eyes moved over the grass to the house. The front door was open and she saw Adrian come through it and walk to his car. He was too far away to know she was watching him, but she still averted her eyes, then, chiding herself for a fool, she continued to look at him. How tall and distinguished he was! Even at this distance one could not mistake his aloof bearing. Yet it was an aloofness that was only surface-deep; beneath it lay kindness and gentleness. And passion too. Despite his austere appearance, he was an exciting and inventive lover.

What would have happened if she had given in to him the other night? Would he have ended his engagement to Diana or would he, when sanity had returned, have hated himself for allowing passion to overcome reason? She would never know the answer and, unless she wanted to be haunted by him for the rest of her life, she must stop asking herself these questions.

A large ball bounced into her lap and with a start she

jerked back, laughing as Tim flung himself upon her. 'Play with us, Tanya,' he shrieked happily. 'Play with us!'

Glad to have other thoughts to occupy her, Tanya jumped to her feet and complied.

A couple of days later she spent the day with Mrs Poulton. Betty and her husband took the children to the seaside for the day and though they asked Tanya to go with them, she decided it would be good for the young couple to be alone with their family. It might even encourage Betty into making a decision to live in her own home instead of sharing her mother's.

Her day was spent happily helping Mrs Poulton bottle forty pounds of jam. It brought back happy memories of the time when she had helped her mother in a similar way, but she did not say this aloud, knowing that to talk of it might reduce her to tears, and if Mrs Poulton occasionally looked at her face and wondered why there were shadows in the lovely eyes, she was too wise to comment.

But when they were sitting down having a well-earned rest, the woman referred to her son and Tanya's friendship with him. 'You've been a good influence on him, Tanya. I wish you and he could settle down together.'

'We don't love each other,' said Tanya. 'We are good friends, nothing more.'

'Pity. You'll make a lovely daughter-in-law.'

'I'm sure he'll bring you one.'

'There's never been any shortage of women for him,' his mother agreed. 'But none of them have brought out the best in him—the way you have. With Diana, for example, he's like a bear with a sore head.'

Tanya was surprised. 'I did not know they still saw each other.'

'They don't—leastways not often. They used to be close as bread and butter when they were kids. Adrian Chesterton too. Now they're not even friends.'

'Is it often like that in England?'

'It's like that all over the world. Even husbands and wives can grow apart, so why shouldn't friends?'

Even husbands and wives ... Tanya was glad Mrs Poulton didn't know the significance of her casually spoken words. One day she would tell the woman about Adrian, but for the moment she dared not do so.

'Do you see much of Diana?' Mrs Poulton asked.

'No. Mr Chesterton is out a great deal and—and Diana goes with him.'

'I suppose they're a devoted couple?'

'Not by Rovnian standards,' Tanya said with a faint smile. 'English people are not demonstrative.'

'I wouldn't say that,' Mrs Poulton replied, though what else she would have said was never uttered, for at that moment Brian rushed in demanding his tea.

Soon the family arrived and they sat around a table laden with ham, salad, a huge bowl of freshly picked tomatoes and several pots of the jam they had just made.

Roger was the last to arrive and he settled himself next to Tanya. 'How do you think our plebeian high tea compares with the Chesterton dinner?' he asked.

'I do not think they can be compared,' she replied slowly. 'One likes what one is accustomed to. In my country we do not have either. We have a big lunch with many courses and we take much longer to eat it—two hours at the least. Then in the evening we have cold meat and salad or a cheese dish with wine and coffee. But now I am accustomed to your way of eating and I think the high tea and then dinner are agreeable—both.'

Everyone laughed and Mrs Poulton gave Roger an old-fashioned look. 'There you are, son. In her own way, Tanya is saying exactly what I did the other day when Diana was here. You can't put people into little boxes these days. Traditions and customs—whether they're of class or country—have been broken down far more quickly than you're willing to admit.'

'And a good thing too,' said Louisa, Roger's youngest sister.

But Tanya was only half listening, her mind pre-occupied with the knowledge that Diana had been here only a few days ago. It was strange Roger had not mentioned it. Unless Diana had come here for personal reasons. She glanced at Roger and saw him watching her, almost as if he guessed what she was thinking.

Before either of them could speak, the telephone rang, bringing with it news that put every other thought out of their heads. Marjorie, Mrs Poulton's eldest daughter, had been rushed to hospital where her baby, not due for another month, was obviously intending to put in an appearance.

'I must go to her at once,' said Mrs Poulton, one hand clutched against her throat.

'There's no need to worry,' Roger put in. 'Peter said she's perfectly all right.'

'I still want to go to her.'

'Would you like me to come with you?' Tanya asked.

'I'll come as well,' said Louise.

'No, you won't. You've got evening classes,' her mother said firmly, 'and Beth's got to stay with Brian. I don't like leaving him in the house alone at night.'

Still talking, Mrs Poulton hurried down the narrow garden path to Roger's car and the three of them set off for the market town of Little Compton, and the hospital.

'I'm sure Marjorie will be fine,' said Tanya. 'I expect

she just has a very impatient little boy!'

Mrs Poulton did not look reassured, and her anxiety only lessened when, at eleven-thirty that night, Peter junior put in an appearance.

Looking through the glass wall into the room where all the newborn infants were housed, Tanya was hard pressed not to cry. It was at times like these that she felt the loneliness of the alien.

'Home and bed for you,' Roger murmured, tucking his arm through hers. 'Why does the arrival of a baby make all women weepy?'

She laughed and her moment of sadness evaporated. Roger kept up a fund of small talk until he had deposited his mother outside her front door, but as soon as he was alone in the car with Tanya he referred to Diana.

'I suppose you're wondering why she came to see me?'

'I'd forgotten all about it,' she replied truthfully. 'Was it because of us?'

'Yes.'

'Adrian was disturbed too. He was angry with me.'

'Do you want us to say goodbye till after the election?'

'No.'

'Good.' Roger drew the car to a stop outside Park Gates. 'I wish we loved each other, Tanya. We'd make a great couple!'

Entering the house, Tanya was aware of the lateness of the hour and quietly hurried to her bedroom. She had almost reached it when she saw Adrian come out of his room, and though she tried to draw back into an alcove, he saw her and came towards her, tall and forbidding in a dark blue dressing-gown.

'You're late,' he stated. 'We were worried about you.'

'We?' she asked pointedly.

'I was.' He paused. 'You've never stayed out so late. I suppose you were with Poulton?'

'I was with Roger and his family.' She stressed the last part of her sentence, but there was no lightening of his expression. 'One of Mrs Poulton's daughters had a baby and I went with her to the hospital.'

'Doesn't she have enough daughters of her own to keep her company?'

'She wanted me.' Tanya looked at him defiantly. 'Do you find that so hard to understand—that somebody wants me?'

His expression grew bleak. 'Why do you persist in quarrelling with me? Don't you think it's difficult for me too, having you here?'

'I don't know how you think,' she said wearily. 'You're a stranger to me.'

But as she spoke she knew she was not being honest. Standing close to him she was able to remember the emotions he had aroused in her. Without realising it she swayed towards him, then drew back quickly, ashamed of her weakness. But he did not see the movement towards him; he saw only the swift way in which she recoiled.

'I wish you didn't hate me so much,' he said quietly.

'I don't hate you.' She half turned away from him. 'It's late, Adrian, I want to go to bed.'

He walked with her down the corridor, pausing when he reached his own room. 'Have you decided what you'll do when you leave here?' he asked.

She shrugged. 'In the last few years I have learned to take one step at a time. And leaving here will be a major step for me.'

'There's no reason why you should go,' he said abruptly. 'You could still stay.'

'After you marry Diana?' Jealousy goaded her into

further speech. 'Do you want me to be nursemaid to your children?'

Colour suffused his face. 'What a swine you must think me! I don't know why I said what I did. But I was thinking of you—of your not being alone.'

'I won't be alone.'

'What does that mean?'

Tanya had made her reply unthinkingly, but now anger decided her to hurt him.

'It means I have no intention of pining for you for the rest of my life. You aren't the only one who will marry again and find happiness.'

'Roger Poulton,' he muttered. 'It hasn't taken you long to fall in love with someone else, then.'

'You should be glad for me. At least I won't be on your conscience.'

'You were never on my conscience. What happened to us was beyond our control. You can blame it on your government; on the fact that you couldn't leave your parents and follow me—but in all honesty I don't think you can blame it on *me*.'

Because she agreed with him she found her anger ebbing and, as it died away, it was replaced by weariness. 'You're right, Adrian. I think it might be better if we don't have conversations late at night. It seems we both say things we regret.'

'I don't regret that I married you,' he said softly. 'I only regret that it didn't work out.'

Swiftly she ran from him, wishing he had left these thoughts unspoken. But they remained with her throughout the night, making it impossible for her to sleep, and at dawn she dressed and went to sit by the window, where she watched the sky lighten over the horizon and saw the dark earth turn from grey to green. Adrian's land; where his children would walk and his wife would be loved.

The knowledge filled her with a pain that was some-how too deep for tears and, dry-eyed, she remained staring through the window.

CHAPTER SEVEN

HARD though he tried, Roger found it impossible to stop thinking of Diana. Her visit to his home had stirred memories that had lain dormant for years, making him recollect the happy times they had shared together as children; the thoughts he had entertained as a teenager, before university and finishing school had parted them. What a pity that, in assuming adult status, people also assumed a different code of behaviour—and not their own code either! Often it was foisted on them by some-one else—as in Diana's case. Yes, there was no doubt her father—autocratic old moneybags that he was—was a great influence on her life.

Adrian had remained a friend far longer, only the course of their different careers finally severing their relationship. With Diana it had been different. Almost overnight—or so it seemed to him in retrospect—she had changed from the determined little girl who had begged him and Adrian to let her play with them into a reserved and distant teenager who had made no move to seek him out when she had come home from her Swiss school. Yet she had continued to see Adrian. It was that which had rankled the most.

Without being aware of it he stopped walking, and only when he felt the heat of the sun shining on the top of his head did he realise he had paused by the stile that led to a short cut to Lord Biddell's property. With a shake of his head, he resumed walking. It was unusual for him to be in the woods at this time of the day, but he had unexpectedly felt the need to be on his own and, refusing to take one more call from a telephone that never seemed to stop ringing, he had escaped from the house.

In the distance he saw the figure of a woman approaching and, reluctant to break his solitude, he swung down to the copse. Unfortunately, she had the same idea, but by then she was close enough to be recognised, and with a sigh he greeted her as she went to walk past him.

'Hello, Diana, aren't you going to talk to me?'

'We said enough the last time we met.'

'That's what I wanted to talk to you about. I owe you an apology.'

'Thank you.' She made to move on, but he still barred her way.

'Why the hurry?' He pointed to an overturned log a few yards away. 'Sit down and relax.'

Silently following him over to the log, she did so.

'I don't know why I lost my temper with you the other day,' he went on abruptly. 'My only excuse is that your visit took me by surprise.'

'You made that plain. It obviously never dawned on you it wasn't easy for me to go on seeing you once I started to grow up.'

'I know your father wouldn't have approved, but——'

'It had nothing to do with my father,' she cut in. 'It was *you*.'

'How come?'

'Because you're five years older than I am. It didn't bother me when we were children, but it made a lot of difference once you were at university.'

'It didn't affect your friendship with Adrian. You still went on seeing him.'

'Because our families were friends.' She gave him a sideways glance and then quickly averted her face. 'You were always so busy with your work and politics,' she continued, 'that it made me very conscious how childish I was.'

It was an explanation Roger had never thought of, and surprise held him captive.

'I don't care if you don't believe me,' she said, misreading his silence, 'you've always enjoyed thinking the worst of me.'

'Don't let's quarrel again,' he muttered. 'I've already had one wigging from my mother!'

Diana smiled slightly. 'She always did loathe bad manners or bullying.'

'And still does,' he said wryly. 'Do you remember the time I made you climb old Jenkins' tree and pinch his apples?'

'I'll never forget the thrashing she gave you when she found out!' Diana admitted.

'But you were a better climber than I was,' he grinned. 'You had longer legs.' He glanced at them and she coloured and pulled at her skirt. 'You don't need to hide them. They're just as lovely now. It's the only part of you that hasn't changed.'

'I haven't changed, Roger. You're the one who's done that.'

'Village boy makes good,' he said sourly. 'Is that what you mean?'

'Not quite in those terms,' she said lightly. 'But then I was never as sorry for you as you were for yourself.' She heard his indrawn breath and gave him a cool look. 'You are, you know. That's why you're on the defensive with me. The only difference between us is one of your own making. You're the one who's put up the barriers.

But then you like to have something to vault over. It makes you feel good.'

'Have you quite finished?' he demanded.

'No.' Now she had started, she seemed to have lost all inhibitions. 'I can see you in ten years' time: carrying a ministerial briefcase but still wearing an old crumpled suit as proof that you haven't forgotten your humble origins! I hate people who believe they have to keep waving their past at you.'

He opened his mouth to say something, thought better of it and tightly clamped his lips. The silence lengthened and he kicked moodily at some twigs.

'Why are we quarrelling, Diana? When you were a kid we used to be friends.'

'I'm not your enemy now.'

'We're on different sides.'

'That still doesn't make me your enemy.'

'Do you honestly think I'm taking Tanya out in order to pump her about Adrian?' he asked suddenly.

This time it was Diana who allowed the silence to last for several moments before she replied. 'It seemed feasible at the time,' she confessed, 'but—but not any more. I can understand why you like seeing her. She's a very beautiful woman.'

'She also has the gift of understanding.'

'Meaning I haven't?'

'I wasn't particularising.' He turned towards her. 'Why do you always assume I'm attacking you?'

'Because I get the feeling you are.'

'Maybe I'm on the defensive with you,' he said abruptly. 'You're a tantalising female.'

Diana jumped up, but he rose at the same time and they found themselves standing close together.

'You're acting as if you're afraid of me,' he said softly.

'Why should I be?'

'I'll show you,' he said thickly, and pulled her into his arms.

His kiss was fiercely passionate, as if desire had been building up in him and been instantly released by the touch of her. It was a touch that he savoured like a gourmet at a three-star restaurant. He slowly caressed shoulders and her back; his body pressed itself to the slim length of hers and his lips moved over her eyes and cheeks and temples, while his nostrils breathed deep of her fragrance.

'Diana,' he said shakily. 'Diana.'

Docilely she remained within his hold, knowing it was useless to fight him and lacking the impetus even to try. She sought to make her mind numb, but her body was tinglingly aware of his; of the hard wall of his chest pressing against her breasts; the roughness of his skin against her face and the warmth of his breath as it mingled with hers. Slowly, insiduously, desire for him awakened in her and the numbness that held her mind gave way to a pulsating longing that was unlike anything she had ever experienced. Then with a little cry she pushed at his chest. He resisted the movement, but as her hands continued to beat at him, he let her go and stepped back. But their eyes remained locked together: his blurred, as if they were still seeing her surrender; hers dark with despair.

'You had no right to do that,' she whispered.

'Why not? A cat may look at a queen!'

'Don't!' she cried. 'Please, Roger, don't!'

Long after Diana had run from the wood, Roger remained where he was, trying and failing to assess his feelings. What was there about Diana that made him behave like a lout? Was it because he wished to destroy her air of touch-me-not, or because she aroused a deeper, more primitive streak in him? Yet he was no tinder box with other women. On the contrary, he had often been accused of having too much control. Wryly he shook his head. That was something Diana would never be able to accuse him of! It looked as if he owed her another apology. But this time when he made it, he would give her no more cause for complaint.

That same evening, Tanya went with him to one of his meetings. As always she sat among the audience, and afterwards gave him her impression of how it had gone.

'I thought you spoke better than I have ever heard you,' she said as they drove away from the hall. 'You were far more explanatory and less—bullying is not the right word, but I do not know what other one to use.'

'Hectoring,' he said. 'That's what my family always accuse me of doing. I can't help it, though. If I feel things deeply I get intense about them.'

'It is better to feel things too deeply than not to feel at all.'

He gave her a sideways glance. 'Are you speaking from experience?'

'It is better than speaking from ignorance!'

Roger gave a short laugh. 'I wish everybody remembered that—including me!' He slowed the car even more. 'How about a drink at the Cap and Bells? I'm beginning to feel guilty that each time I ask you out, you have to hear me hector!'

'I enjoy listening to you,' she assured him.

'How do I compare with Adrian?' From the corner of his eye he saw her give a slight start and said hastily: 'Forget the question. I'd no business asking it.'

'I would be happy to answer it, but—but I've never heard him speak.'

'Well, I'm damned! I suppose he takes it for granted

you'll vote for him whether you hear him or not?'

'I do not have a vote,' she smiled. 'I have not been here long enough.'

He was still chuckling at this as they entered the private bar of the Cap and Bells. It was the first time Tanya had been inside an English public house and she looked curiously at the shaded lights and polished oak furniture. 'It is nice here. Always I thought a pub had bare floors and many people.'

'They do,' Roger agreed. 'But saloon bars are better furnished and quiet. You might even find a princess coming here.'

'A princess?'

'Diana,' Roger explained, looking uncomfortable.

'Why do you not like her?'

'I do like her,' he said shortly, 'but she's different from us.'

'She breathes and eats and sleeps the way we do,' said Tanya. 'I think your Shakespeare put it better, but you know what I mean.'

'Shylock in *The Merchant of Venice*,' Roger replied. 'I know exactly what you mean. But Diana isn't like us, any more than Adrian is.'

'You wouldn't talk this way if you lived in my country,' Tanya burst out. 'Anyone who is not *for* our government is automatically considered an enemy and put in prison. But here it doesn't matter which side you are on. You all have your freedom!'

'You'll be telling me next it doesn't matter who we vote for!' Roger retorted.

'I'm not sure it does. You and Adrian are both good men.'

'I don't appreciate being compared with Adrian.'

'Why not?' she asked crossly.

'Because he's overbearing and ice-cold.'

'He's nothing of the sort! He's just learned how to hide his feelings.'

'He doesn't have any.'

'Of course he does! Do you think I'd have married a man who——'

With horror Tanya realised what she had said. But it was impossible to draw back the words, nor was there any way in which she could deny them. Their truth was too evident in her expression. Desperately she looked at Roger, knowing she had to obtain his promise of silence.

'Please forget what I said,' she begged. 'It is not my secret to give away.'

'Not your secret ...?' He shook his head dazedly. 'You mean you're Adrian's wife?'

'Please!' Fear shook her. 'Keep your voice down. No one must hear.'

Seeing her anguished expression, his own softened. 'Don't you think you should tell me the whole story, Tanya? It's the least you can do.'

She nodded and wondered where to begin. 'I met him in Rovnia,' she said slowly. 'It was the day of the Rose Carnival. ...'

Roger listened to Tanya's story with no outward sign of emotion, and only when she reached her arrival at Park Gates did his anger explode. 'What a filthy way to treat you!'

'People do strange things when they are caught in a trap,' she said.

'That still doesn't justify his behaviour. You should never have done as he asked.'

'I did it because——' She stopped and glanced over her shoulder. 'What was that?'

'What?'

'I thought I heard the door open.'

Roger peered past her. 'There's nobody there.' He

turned to face her again. 'I still think you were crazy to do as Adrian wanted.'

'But I understood the problem he had. You must not condemn him because he married me and then regretted it.'

'It isn't the fact that he regretted it that makes me angry. It's the way he's tried to get rid of you—to pretend you're his sister's nanny ... Damn it, Tanya, he deserves everything he gets, and if you let me use this information, I'll make damn sure he doesn't win the election.'

'You mustn't!' She stared at him in horror. 'I gave him my word I'd keep it a secret. If he discovers I've betrayed him ... Oh, Roger, promise you won't say anything.'

Roger's eyes became narrow blue slits. 'If that's the way you feel, there's nothing more to be said. I think you're wrong, but I'll respect your wishes.'

'I don't want you to respect them,' she said. 'I want you to understand them. People change—as you know very well—and you can't blame Adrian because he stopped loving me. After all, he thought I had divorced him and——'

'You needn't excuse him,' Roger said abruptly. 'I've given you my word and I won't break it.' He rubbed the side of his jaw, his lids lowered over his eyes. 'I take it Diana knows who you are?'

'Yes.'

'Then that's why she asked me not to see you. She's in a tricky position too.'

'Only until the legal position is cleared up. Then they will be free to marry.'

'It beats me how you and Diana can defend him,' Roger muttered.

'What would you have done in Adrian's position?'

Tanya demanded. 'He wants to win the election as much as you do, and he was afraid that if you found out about me, you'd use it against him.'

'I still don't believe I'd have acted in the same way,' Roger said slowly. 'Nor would I have got engaged to another girl without first making sure I was legally divorced.'

'It's only a technicality,' Tanya explained. 'Once the election is over, he'll get his freedom.'

'And the prince and princess will live happily ever after.'

'Yes,' Tanya forced herself to say. 'Although Diana is so reserved, I think she loves Adrian very much.'

'Do you?' Roger said in such an odd tone that Tanya stared at him.

'Don't you?' she asked.

'I don't know what Diana feels. Except that she isn't as reserved as she pretends.' He rose. 'Fancy another drink? I don't know about you, but I can do with one.'

She shook her head and watched as he went over to the bar. Whenever Roger spoke of Diana he was always on the defensive, as if expecting to be attacked. Did he feel the girl was his enemy because they were on different political sides? Yet why should it matter to him if this were so? Tanya continued to watch him as he waited for his drink. It wasn't only Roger's attitude to Diana that was strange but Diana's attitude to *him*. Tanya remembered how the girl had demanded that she stopped seeing him. At the time she had not understood Diana's anger, but now she found herself searching for a different reason for it. Could Diana—and Roger too—be fighting something far more basic and emotional than a by-election? Like love?

It was a fantastic theory that quickly became believable fact. Everything pointed to its truth. Diana's anger against Roger; Roger's bitterness towards Adrian, which had always struck her as being a deeper cause than political differences.

Roger returned to their table holding a glass of beer. He sipped and gave her a slight smile. But the smile did not reach his eyes. Tanya looked at him as though seeing him for the first time; and in a way she felt she was. He was too thin for his height, and even though normally pale-skinned, at the moment it had a greyish tinge to it, as if he had had too many anxious days and sleepless nights.

'Why are you looking at me with such big eyes?' he asked. 'If you're still worrying I'll give away Adrian's secret, then forget it. I promise you I won't.'

'I was not thinking of Adrian,' she confessed, 'but of you and Diana.'

With the glass halfway to his mouth he paused and put it down carefully, as if he were afraid he might spill it. 'What about Diana and me?'

Unused to modern prevarication, and with the bluntness of her race, Tanya said: 'I think you love each other.'

'For God's sake! That's such a crazy suggestion I won't even bother to deny it.'

'I'm glad,' said Tanya, referring only to the last part of his answer, 'because I'm sure I'm right.'

'Women always think that,' he said with an attempt at humour.

'When a man loves a woman there is something in his voice when he says her name that always gives him away. Whether or not you admit it, you love Diana. I——' She stopped short as the bar door opened and a middle-aged man with a bush of greying hair approached them. She recognised him as Roger's election agent.

'Hello, Bob,' Roger said. 'I don't think you've met Miss Kovacs. Tanya, this is Bob Edwards.'

Tanya's hand was taken in a hard grip as the man said hello and then joined them at the table. For the next half hour he talked to Roger about the rallies he had planned, and the various problems which their canvassers had discovered, and when a distant clock chimed the hour, Tanya used it as an excuse to say she wanted to go home. It made her feel disloyal to Adrian to sit here and listen to his rivals talk so positively about winning the election.

'You needn't bother seeing me home,' she said. 'You and Mr Edwards have things to talk over and——'

'It's nothing that can't wait.' Roger glanced at his agent. 'I'll see you at the Committee rooms in the morning.'

'Fine.' The man took out the stub of a cigarette from his pocket and was carefully lighting it as Tanya and Roger left him.

'I do not think I like your agent,' Tanya commented as they drove towards Park Gates. 'He does not seem honest.'

'He's no more dishonest than most of his breed. You're just not used to the type.'

'That is so,' she agreed. 'I know only teachers and professors—like my father.'

'Do you miss your life in Rovnia?' Roger asked, for the first time referring to the story she had told him earlier that evening.

'I miss the life I used to have—when I was a child and in my early teens—but I do not miss what Rovnia is today.'

Roger grunted, as though not sure what to say, and she was relieved when she could finally leave him and enter the house. She had no fear that he would break the word that he had given her, but nonetheless she still regretted the slip of the tongue which had forced her into telling him the truth.

Roger himself was in far less sanguine a mood as he set off for home. He found it impossible to forget what Tanya had told him about Adrian. In spite of their differences in outlook, he had always respected the man, but now he felt contempt for the way he had behaved towards the woman he had once professed to love and who was also still his wife. Yet Tanya wouldn't hear a word against him; obviously loved him still. It beat him how she could. But then women could love the most unsuitable of men. Like Diana, for instance. If Tanya was right and Diana loved *him*.... But no, that was impossible. His momentary elation gave way to anger and he savagely pressed his foot on the accelerator, forcing the ancient car to its maximum speed. Only when he came to the village and was forced to slow down did he again remember all Tanya had said about Diana. But it was nonsense! She no more loved him than he loved her.

With a squeal of brakes he brought the car to an abrupt halt outside his front gate. He didn't love a toffee-nosed little aristocrat like Diana Biddell! It was a preposterous idea.

He banged the front door violently behind him, forgetful of the lateness of the hour and the sleeping occupants of the house, his whole being so intent on refuting all Tanya had said that he was unaware of anything else.

CHAPTER EIGHT

Two days later Adrian strode angrily into his home and slammed the door hard behind him. The sound brought Diana running from the library, her expression showing concern at such unusual behaviour.

'Is anything wrong Adrian?'

'Everything. It's all over the county that Tanya's my wife!'

'What!' The envelopes Diana had been holding slipped to the floor and she bent automatically to pick them up. 'Who—who did it?'

'Who do you think?' he said irritably. 'Obviously Poulton.'

'I don't believe Tanya told him.'

'She loves him,' Adrian said. 'That's why she did it.'

Diana looked down at the envelopes. 'What are you going to do?'

'What can I do? I can't deny it, can I? But I'm damned if I'm going to let her stay here. She can pack her bags and go!'

'If you send her away you'll be playing into Roger's hands.'

'What do you suggest I do—introduce her around the constituency?'

'You might have to.'

Adrian was amazed; not because the idea was new to him—he had thought of it himself the moment he had heard the news—but because he had not expected Diana to make such a suggestion.

'Are you saying I should acknowledge her as my wife when I'm supposed to be engaged to you?'

'You have no choice,' Diana said quietly.

'And where will you fit into all this?'

'I won't. For the time being we'll have to forget our engagement. In the circumstances, it's the only thing we can do.'

The look he gave her was long and steady and held far more admiration than ever before. 'You've behaved wonderfully all through these last difficult weeks,' he said quietly, 'but I never thought you'd be called on to.... Dammit, I could strangle Tanya!'

'That would give Roger the election on a plate!' A faint smile curved Diana's lips. 'It might have been better all round if we'd broken off our engagement when Tanya arrived here.'

'Are you saying that because of my career,' he asked, 'or because you've decided you don't love me?' She was so long replying that he came over and put his hand on her shoulder. 'Don't you love me, Diana? I know I haven't been a very satisfactory fiancé, but——'

'Neither have I,' she interrupted. 'As to whether or not I love you ... I don't know, Adrian. We've never talked about love before. We got engaged because we both wanted a home and children, but you can't honestly say you feel for me the way you felt when you married Tanya!'

Abruptly he turned away from her, and it was a few seconds before he replied. 'I'll never feel for any woman what I felt for Tanya. I wouldn't let myself go through that sort of thing again.'

'You talk as if one can decide whether or not to fall in love,' she said drily.

'I think one can. Not when you're young, perhaps, but

certainly when you're older—when you've already been hurt. I'm sorry I have to say this,' he continued gently, 'but it isn't fair for you to marry me expecting something I'll never be able to give you.'

'Why didn't you say this when you asked me to be your wife?' she said.

'Because at the time I didn't think you'd want more from me. But now I'm not so sure. Perhaps I wouldn't allow myself to see that you were still young and had a right to expect roses and blue skies.'

'Instead of which you're telling me that all you can offer me are clouds and nettles.'

He was faintly surprised that she could joke about it and not sure that he liked it. Still, perhaps it was better to keep things light. Lord knew he'd had more than his fill of emotion.

'Your original opinion of me was correct, Adrian,' Diana went on. 'I'm quite aware that your feelings for me aren't the—aren't the ones you felt for Tanya, and quite frankly I wouldn't like it if they were. I'm not passionately in love with you either and—and I think that if we both realise it, we'll have a better chance of being happy.' Unexpectedly her lower lip started to tremble and she bit hard on it. 'I don't believe in love that bowls you over so completely that you forget everything else. I don't want my life to be upset by a lot of unnecessary emotion.'

'What are you afraid of?' Adrian sensed a deeper meaning behind her words. 'Emotion doesn't necessarily have to be destructive. It can be deeply satisfying.'

'*You're* happy to live without it.'

'Because I've been hurt.'

'Perhaps I'm afraid of being hurt too.'

'Perhaps you're afraid of life,' he corrected gently. 'Your father's always been so——'

SAVE TIME, TROUBLE & MONEY!
By joining the exciting NEW...

Mills & Boon 🌹
Romance
CLUB

WITH
all these
EXCLUSIVE BENEFITS
for every member

NOTHING TO PAY! MEMBERSHIP IS FREE TO REGULAR READERS!

IMAGINE the *pleasure* and *security* of having ALL your favourite *Mills & Boon* romantic fiction delivered right to *your* home, absolutely POST FREE ... straight off the press! No waiting! No more disappointments! All this PLUS all the latest news of *new books* and *top-selling authors* in your own monthly MAGAZINE ... PLUS *regular* big CASH SAVINGS ... PLUS lots of wonderful strictly-limited, *members-only* SPECIAL OFFERS! All these exclusive benefits can be *yours* – right NOW – simply by joining the exciting NEW *Mills & Boon* ROMANCE CLUB. Complete and post *this whole card* for FREE full-colour leaflet. It costs nothing. HURRY!

No obligation to join unless you wish!

FREE FULL COLOUR LEAFLET!
JUST COMPLETE SECTION BELOW. THEN CUT-OFF AND POST THIS WHOLE CARD!

FREE CLUB MAGAZINE
Packed with advance news of latest titles and authors

Exciting offers of
FREE BOOKS
For club members ONLY

Lots of fabulous
BARGAIN OFFERS
–many at
BIG CASH SAVINGS

To: MILLS & BOON READER SERVICE, P.O. Box No 236, 14 Sanderstead Road, South Croydon, Surrey CR2 9PU, England. WITHOUT OBLIGATION to join, please send me FREE details of the exciting NEW **Mills & Boon** ROMANCE CLUB and of all the exclusive benefits of membership.

Please write in BLOCK LETTERS below

NAME (Mrs/Miss) ....

ADDRESS ....

CITY/TOWN ....

COUNTY/COUNTRY .... POST/ZIP CODE ....

RC/5/78/RS

POST-FREE CARD-No stamp is needed! *(See over)*

— — — — — — — CUT-OFF ALONG HERE — — — — — — —

Do not affix postage stamps if posted in
Gt. Britain, Channel Islands or N. Ireland.

Postage will
be paid by
Mills & Boon
Limited

BUSINESS REPLY SERVICE
Licence No. CN.81

Romance Club, (Dept RCC),
MILLS & BOON READER SERVICE,
P.O. Box No. 236
14 Sanderstead Road,
SOUTH CROYDON,
SURREY, CR2 9PU.

'Please leave Father out of it,' she said sharply. 'You're the second person to hint that I'm father-fixated, and it's beginning to annoy me.'

Adrian was curious to know who the first person had been, but forbore to ask. 'I'd like to continue this conversation another time,' he said quietly, 'but with a wife waiting on the sidelines, it isn't exactly opportune.'

He moved towards the stairs, stopping as he saw Tanya coming down them. 'I was coming to look for you,' he said icily. 'I suppose you know why?' He saw her creamy skin pale and the anger he had thought to control erupted again. 'Doesn't giving your word mean anything to you?' he demanded. 'Are you so anxious for Poulton to win that you had to break your promise?'

'I didn't break it,' she whispered. 'He found out by accident. He promised ... he swore he wouldn't tell anyone.'

'He's told *everyone*! Did you think he wouldn't?'

'I don't believe Roger broke his word,' Diana intervened.

'So he's found a champion in you!' said Adrian, swinging round on her.

'I'm not his champion.' Diana's face was flushed, but she would not back down. 'Until you were on opposite sides, you and Roger were friends. Surely you know he wouldn't do anything underhand?'

'We're not discussing what we used to be,' Adrian retorted. 'All I'm concerned with is what we *are*. And you know the facts as well as I do. He found out that Tanya's my wife and he's made sure everyone else knows it.'

'You're wrong!' Tanya cried, and turned on her heel.

'Where are you going?' Adrian called.

'To see Roger.'

'You can't. Don't be stupid, Tanya!'

But she took no heed of him and raced across the hall to the drive. Adrian called her again, but she refused to turn back and, afraid he might come after her, she swung across the lawn and disappeared between the trees.

She was hot and dishevelled by the time she reached Roger's house and she banged on the knocker, praying he would be in. Luck was with her and Roger himself came to the door. One glance at her face and he drew her into the small room he used as his office.

'You've heard, then?' he said.

'Yes,' she cried. 'How could you?'

'I didn't,' he said heavily. 'It was Bob Edwards. You remember when we were talking in the Cap and Bells and you thought you heard the door to the bar open?'

'You mean it was him?'

'Yes. He wanted to speak to me, but when he heard you mention Adrian's name he stopped and listened. Then he waited a bit before coming in.'

'That's why his manner was strange,' Tanya muttered. 'I knew I didn't like him, and I was right.'

Roger laughed without humour. 'There's something to feminine intuition after all.'

'I owe you an apology,' she said. 'I'm sorry I believed you had broken your word.'

'Forget it,' he shrugged. 'Anyone would have thought the same.'

'Diana didn't.'

Roger rubbed the side of his face but gave no other sign that he had heard what Tanya had said.

Tanya sat down on a chair, not because she wanted to remain there but because her legs did not feel as if they could support her. 'What are people saying about Adrian and me?'

'Nothing very good,' Roger admitted. 'They know

you're a Rovnian and that Adrian left you after you were married.'

'He had no choice,' she stated. 'He was sent back to England and I was unable to go with him. He never deserted me.'

'You don't need to defend him to me,' Roger said gently. 'But you asked me what people are saying and I've told you. Bob wanted to discredit Adrian and he's succeeded. You've got to admit Adrian's played into his hands. Having you hide your identity and pretend to be his sister's nanny was a pretty lousy thing to do.'

Tanya could not disagree. Yet she still saw it from Adrian's point of view. With a heavy sigh she rose and went to the door. 'Sometimes I wish I'd never escaped from Rovnia!'

'You mustn't say that.' Roger was beside her, his expression concerned. 'In a little while you'll look back on all this as if it were a bad dream. You've got your life ahead of you, Tanya. You can't let the mistake you made when you were young ruin your entire future.'

'My marriage to Adrian wasn't a mistake,' she said. 'That's the trouble. He's the one who regrets it, not me.'

'I'll never understand women,' Roger muttered as he walked with her to the gate and offered to drive her home, an offer which she refused. 'After the way he treated you, I'd have thought you'd despise him.'

'Sometimes I do. But it doesn't stop me loving him.'

'What's going to happen now?'

'I'll do anything he wants,' she said slowly. 'At least I owe him that.'

'You owe him nothing. And if he goes on blaming you for what happened, pack your things and come here. You're welcome to stay with us for as long as you like.'

Tanya smiled wanly. 'If I did that, I'd really be giving Adrian reason to hate me.'

Bidding Roger goodbye, she returned to Park Gates. Voices were coming from the drawing-room and hearing her own name mentioned, she knew the family were discussing the latest turn of events.

Suddenly Betty's voice rose above the others. 'Personally speaking, I think it's about time you recognised her. She's behaved jolly well and——'

'Which is more than I have, I suppose?' Adrian's voice cut in angrily.

'You said it, not me,' his sister replied. 'If your marriage was a mistake, then by all means rectify it. But at least do so with honour.'

'Betty! Adrian! Mrs Chesterton expostulated. 'You're both not facing facts. Once the election is over Adrian can——'

'Damn the election!' It was Adrian again. 'You can't expect people to put their emotions into cold storage while they sort out their political life.'

'That's *exactly* what I expect them to do,' his mother replied, 'and it's what you were doing until this awful story leaked out.'

'The only thing awful about it,' Adrian replied quietly, 'is the way I behaved. I don't hold Tanya responsible for any of it. It was my fault entirely.'

There was a momentary silence, broken by the sound of chairs being pushed back and then Dick Tufton speaking. 'Come on, Betty, let's go upstairs.'

Unwilling to be caught eavesdropping, Tanya moved quickly across the hall and into the drawing-room.

'So there you are,' said Mrs Chesterton. 'We were talking about you.'

'I heard.' Tanya glanced at Betty and Dick as they

walked out, then went to stand nearer to Adrian. 'Diana was right about Roger. He didn't break his word to me—it was his agent.'

'I see.' Adrian looked at his mother. 'Would you leave us alone, please?' He waited until they were, before continuing. 'It still doesn't alter the position I'm in.'

'I will do whatever I can to help you.'

'Do you mean that?' His eyes were so intense a blue that they looked like pieces of lapis lazuli.

'Of course I mean it. I heard you say a moment ago that you don't blame me, but—but I blame myself.'

'Don't let's use the word blame,' he said abruptly, and then paused as if he found it difficult to continue.

Tanya would have helped him if she could, but she was not sure what he wanted to say. Powerless to direct the course he must take, she went on waiting.

'I'd like you to—to take your place here as—er—as my wife,' he said jerkily. 'We can say we kept your arrival here a secret because we were concerned for the safety of the people who had helped you escape. It's the only story I can think of, but it might work.'

'It might.'

'You don't sound enthused,' he said drily.

'Do you expect me to care about the success of your career? I'm only helping you because I want to be able to leave here with a clear conscience.'

'That's all right, then,' he said curtly. 'At least we both know where we stand. The only other thing I'd like to make clear is that my behaviour to you when you arrived had nothing to do with the fact that I was fighting a by-election. My engagement to Diana would still have been a barrier between us. I'm only grateful you didn't turn up after I'd already married her!'

All Tanya's anger evaporated, leaving her desolately

acknowledging the truth of what Adrian had said. Their estrangement had nothing to do with his career. It was his engagement to another woman which had come between them.

'Forgive me, Tanya,' Adrian was speaking again, his expression one of remorse. 'I keep vowing I won't lose my temper with you—but then you say something that makes me so angry that——'

'It's your bad conscience again,' she cut in.

'Yes,' he said curtly. 'I don't like the way things have turned out, but——'

'Don't apologise. In life, nothing stands still. That was something I learned a long time ago.'

'It sounds like a Rovnian proverb.'

'It is.' With the faintest of smiles she slipped from the room, and Adrian stood by the mantelpiece and stared into the empty grate.

Tanya was right. Nothing remained the same. He thought of their marriage and, inexplicably, of her parents, whose love for each other had never faded. It seemed that if one were lucky enough, some things didn't change. Pushing aside such thoughts, for they led him along a path he did not want to travel, he strode into the library where a pile of work awaited him. That was what mattered to him in future. His work and the estate.

And Diana, of course. He must not forget Diana.

CHAPTER NINE

ALTHOUGH no longer engaged to Adrian, Diana still came to the house and went canvassing for him each day. Occasionally she took Tanya with her, and though at first Tanya was embarrassed by it, Diana met all curious glances with equanimity.

It was behaviour Tanya could not understand. Either Diana was so determined Adrian should win the election that she was able to subjugate her own feelings for him, or else she had no feelings for him whatever. The more Tanya considered this, the more convinced she was it was the latter reason.

It was also taken for granted that Tanya would accompany him to many of his meetings, and she found it strange to sit on the platform and listen to him speak. He had none of Roger's grandiloquence, and his speeches lacked the same fire, but there was a sincerity in them which she found moving and a boyish good humour which did as much to discredit his hecklers as all Roger's witty answers.

'I'll be glad when it's over,' she said one afternoon to Diana as they squatted together on the floor in the library among a cloud of pamphlets. 'I still cannot decide whether I agree with Roger or Adrian. To me, they both say many good things.'

'Because they're both good speakers,' Diana said lightly.

Tanya sat back on her heels. 'Do you think Adrian will win?'

'I'm not sure.'

'Did he have a better chance before I came here?'

'Yes,' Diana said awkwardly. 'But don't blame your-self for it. It's just one of those things.'

Tanya marvelled that the girl could be so controlled, but before she could probe it further, Emma and Timmy rushed in.

'Why don't you play with us?' the little girl cried. 'We never see you any more.'

'I'm sorry, darling.' Tanya hugged Emma close. 'But I'm busy helping Uncle Adrian.'

'You never used to help him.'

'I promise I'll play with you on Saturday afternoon. If it's a nice day, I'll take you out somewhere.'

'I've got a present for you,' Tim piped up and, catch-ing hold of her hand, deposited a goldfish on it, more dead than alive.

'Timmy!' Tanya cried in horror. 'Where did you get it? The poor thing's nearly dead! We must put it in some water.'

Running over to the desk, she took the flowers out from a vase and dropped the fish in their place. At once it started to swim around.

'He got it from the lily pond,' Emma explained. 'I told him he was naughty, but he wouldn't listen.'

'I's not naughty,' said Timmy, and opened his mouth to howl.

With the speed of remembered usage, Tanya scooped him up in her arms, picked up the vase and marched out of the house to the lily pond. With the goldfish safely restored to its element, she sat by the edge of the pool and watched the children play ball. It was not long before they pleaded with her to join them, and laughing, began to do so. Full of high spirits, the children became

more boisterous and one of Emma's shots sent the ball
shooting up into the air, where it was caught on its
descent by the tall slim figure of a man who had suddenly appeared from behind a clump of bushes. It was
Adrian and, still holding the ball, he advanced towards
them and dropped it into Emma's hand.

'A few more throws like that,' he said, 'and you'll be
playing for England!'

The two children clamoured around him, begging him
to join their game, and after a momentary hesitation, he
did so.

Tanya played awkwardly, aware of Adrian beside her.
But he seemed in no way put out by her presence and
swooped and darted about the lawn, looking years
younger than the forbidding, stern man to whom she had
grown accustomed. How much more he was like the
young man of the past.

A call from the house caused them to stop playing and
they saw Betty waving from the nursery. 'I think
Mummy wants you to go in to tea,' Tanya told the
children and, with lagging steps, they reluctantly obeyed.

Adrian sank down by the side of the pond and mop-
ped his brow. 'I'm out of condition,' he remarked. 'Another year like this and I'll go to seed.'

She frowned. 'Is that not something to do with
flowers?'

He laughed, the first spontaneous one he had given in
her presence. 'It's a colloquialism and means I'm getting
flabby.'

'You are not the type,' she replied and, aware of his
proximity, turned away and pretended to be absorbed
by the water. He was still warm from his exercise and
she felt the heat he emanated almost as if it were
tangible. —

For his part, Adrian was equally conscious of Tanya. How she had altered since arriving here! It was impossible to believe she was the same shabbily dressed waif who had faced him a few months ago. This Tanya was the same girl he had married, with the same charm, the same delicate golden-brown body. She was still keeping her head averted and he looked at the straight line of her nose, the smooth forehead, the full curve of her mouth with its short, endearingly childish upper lip; yet when those lips had moved beneath his, they had responded with the passion of a woman.

As if aware of his gaze, Tanya moved restlessly and her full skirts fanned out around her. They were the same violet as her eyes, and he remembered that on their honeymoon she had worn a violet dress too. It had been on the first day of their marriage and they had gone walking in the mountains and lain together on the grass. Even without closing his eyes, he could still smell that sweet, fresh scent.

'I'll love you all my life,' he had said, and buried his face in her lap.

Looking at her now, he knew an irresistible urge to do the same; to gather her close against him and take succour from her lips. He blinked rapidly and sat up straighter. What was the matter with him? He must be losing his control to let himself think like this. How could he want one woman when he was engaged to another? Of course he could put the question another way and ask how he could be engaged to the other woman, when he still loved the first one. He shook his head. He must watch himself or he would do something he would regret. He was working hard and he was tired; one often had fanciful thoughts on occasions like these.

Abruptly he said: 'Do you know this is almost the

first time we've been alone together without quarrelling?'

'I am learning the art of pretence,' she said composedly.

'Don't ever pretend, Tanya. I always associate you with honesty.'

She looked at him over her shoulder, unconsciously provocative as the sun found her gold-tipped lashes.

'Tell me about your parents,' he said jerkily. 'You never heard from your father, did you—after they took him away?'

'We only heard that he had died. Through a friend's influence we were able to get back his belongings: a gold tie-pin and a cigarette case.' Her voice was calm yet sad. 'To me they are more precious than anything else I possess. I would starve rather than part with them.'

'I'm sure you'll never have to part with them.'

She shrugged. 'They would bring me money if I were to sell them.'

'You won't be in need of money. I've told you I'll take care of you.'

'I want nothing from you after I leave here,' she said firmly. 'I intend to take a job and look after myself.'

'You won't need to work,' Adrian insisted.

'I must. When I leave here. I never want to think of you again.'

His face paled. 'I didn't realise you still hated me. In the last few weeks I had hoped we were friends.'

'We can never be friends,' she said passionately and, at that moment, came closer to hating him than at any time in her life. How could he believe they could ever be friends? Did he think her love for him was as fickle as his had proved to be for her?

'When I leave here, I want to put you out of my mind,'

she reiterated. 'If it were possible to catch amnesia, I would go to a doctor and ask him to inject me with a virus for it! I want to be free of you—to make myself believe I never met you!'

With a flurry of skirts she ran across the lawn. Adrian waited until she had disappeared from sight, then he began to walk in the opposite direction, his thoughts so far away that he did not notice where he was going.

The Tanya of old would never have stormed at him as the new one had. She was no longer the golden girl he had married but a spitfire. With determination he tried to remember her as she had been, but today's Tanya kept intruding on the image and the more he tried to separate them, the more indivisible they became, until he suddenly realised that the Tanya of the past and the present had converged one with the other.

And with this discovery came the knowledge that he loved her. That the emotion he had felt for her eight years ago was the same one he felt today.

His thoughts were so chaotic he was forced to stand still; almost as if his mental state had affected his physical one. Which of course it had. He could see it clearly now. Bitterly hurt when he had learned Tanya had divorced him, he had used all his strength of mind to cut her out of his life and, in succeeding to do so, had numbed his physical senses. Because of that he had believed he had stopped loving her; had been able to look at her as though she were a stranger.

But once she had come back into his life, his numbness had begun to recede and the wall he had built around himself started to crumble. Without realising it he had once more started to respond to her presence; to the beauty that had first aroused him; to the gentleness that had first touched him and, more important still, had found her new maturity and spirit an even greater lure. But he had so indoctrinated himself that he had not realised exactly what was happening to him until it was almost too late.

Almost but not quite. He kicked a stone out of his path and started to walk again. Before he could say anything to Tanya he must first talk to Diana. He did not pretend she would be heartbroken if they did not marry, but the fact remained that he was morally obligated to clear things with her first. Only then could he tell Tanya he loved her.

But though this knowledge warmed him, it did not give him the pleasure he had expected, and he realised that the joy he should have felt was being swamped by guilt. By guilt at having been so cruel to her and by the fear that his cruelty had killed her love for him.

Yet she had loved him when she had first come here, so would it be too hopeful to assume she still felt the same? He tried to assess her actions of the last few weeks, but there was nothing in them to give him the reassurance he was seeking; rather the contrary, for there had been a detachment in her manner towards him that had put up a barrier between them. He wondered what was the best way of breaking it down. If he told her he loved her now she might think he was saying it out of expediency. She was astute enough to know he did not love Diana deeply and might believe Adrian would prefer to continue with his present marriage rather than have the publicity of a divorce.

Grimly he accepted that it would take time and patience to prove his love, but as he walked across the fields he vowed that no matter the effort, he would go on trying until he had won her back.

With an unusual sense of lightheartedness he returned

to the house, though once in the privacy of his room, he sank wearily on to the bed. If only he could go to Tanya this minute and tell her how he felt! But the fear that she would turn him away kept him where he was. No, his earlier decision was the correct one. He must make haste slowly.

He was late down to dinner and entered the drawing-room, to find his mother and Tanya already there.

'You're late,' Mrs. Chesterton commented.

'Does it matter?'

'What an extraordinary answer! You're the one who likes everything to be on time.'

'Then I must stop being so rigid.'

'After the election you'll have to be even more punctual—otherwise you'll never get things done.'

'I may not win,' he said abruptly.

'Of course you'll win. It's a pity you can't find some scandal about Poulton. It's the sort of thing that would help to——'

'I'm sure there's no scandal attached to him,' Adrian interrupted, 'and even if there were, I wouldn't use it.'

'I don't see why not. His agent didn't have any scruples about smearing *your* name!'

'It had nothing to do with Roger. As far as I'm concerned he's never fought dirty, and I don't intend to be the one to start.'

Tanya listened with pleased surprise. She caught Adrian's eye and smiled at him with more warmth than she had recently displayed. He smiled back at her, but there was a sadness in his expression that puzzled her: it was as if he knew the cause of her sudden friendliness and was unhappy about it.

During dinner Tanya listened to the buzz of conversation around her. Betty was a lively conversationalist and she and her mother argued amicably about the cost of children's clothes and whether or not Emma should go to boarding school. It was a subject on which Tanya felt too strongly not to make any comment.

'If children are sent away from home it breaks up family life,' she said.

'Boarding school encourages children to be independent,' said Dick.

'If a child is happy and loved by its parents, it will have a natural independence.'

'Don't you believe it! Most parents try to smother their children with too much affection. Take Betty for example. She's always fussing over them.'

'Because she does not have enough to do.' Tanya stopped in embarrassment, but Betty was not put out.

'You're right, Tanya, and Dick and I have been giving it some thought. In fact now seems as good a time as any to discuss it.' She looked round the table. 'We've decided to find a place of our own.'

'I thought you'd got that silly idea out of your head long ago!' Mrs Chesterton expostulated.

'Why is it silly?'

'Because you have as much privacy here as if you were living alone,' Mrs Chesterton gave Tanya a look of dislike. 'This is your doing, of course. Haven't you caused enough trouble for Adrian without interfering in my daughter's life?'

There was a stunned silence, broken almost at once by Betty. 'Of course Tanya had something to do with it—not so much from what she said, but from the fact that she was here. It made me realise this is Adrian's home, and that when he marries Diana he's entitled to live here without his family hanging round his neck!'

'I'm sure Adrian doesn't feel we're doing that,' Mrs Chesterton replied.

'Do you?' Betty asked her brother.

'I haven't given it any thought,' he said and, glancing at Tanya, knew he would infinitely prefer to have her to himself. 'But actually you're right. Married people need their own place.'

Betty looked pleased. 'I'll start house-hunting right away.'

'So will I,' Mrs Chesterton said frigidly.

'The Dower House will be vacant in November,' Adrian said to his mother.

'It's too big for me.'

'Perhaps we could enlarge it for us?' Betty suggested, and talk ranged round the feasibility of doing this, with Mrs Chesterton moving into another cottage on the estate.

Tanya was glad when dinner was over and they all went into the drawing-room, for here she could seek out a distant chair where she would not feel overwhelmed by Adrian's proximity.

Watching her walk gracefully across the carpet, Adrian knew he had never found her more desirable and longed to kiss away the sadness that caused the curve of her mouth to droop. Remembering his earlier behaviour to her, he knew it was only right that he should have to pay for it. And how high a price it was! Every moment that he had to pretend indifference towards her; every passionate urge he had to forswear; every aching need he had to ignore was a whiplash on his guilty conscience. Perhaps when he had paid in full for his guilt, he might more easily be able to tell Tanya how much he needed her.

Resisting the urge to sit beside her, he made an effort to engage Dick in conversation, not knowing that Tanya misinterpreted his distance as being one of dislike. 'He can't even bear to sit next to me,' she thought miserably and, finding this knowledge stifling, decided to go to her room.

'Where are you going?' Betty asked.

'Upstairs. I have some sewing to do and——'

'How about a walk?' Adrian interrupted.

'I'm too tired.'

He was at the door as she reached it, and he held it open for her. 'Are you sure you won't change your mind?' he asked in so low a tone that no one else could hear. 'It's a beautiful night. The moon's shining and there isn't a cloud in the sky.'

'A night for lovers,' she said involuntarily.

'Yes.' He leaned closer. 'Please come, Tanya.'

'No. You have your women muddled. You should be asking Diana, not me!'

He drew back, his features tight, and she slipped past him and ran up the stairs.

Restlessly she paced her room, her earlier distress magnified by this last conversation with Adrian. What game was he playing that he dared suggest they walked together in the moonlight? She had found herself thinking many harsh things about him in the past months, but she had never considered him a philanderer.

She gave an impatient shake of her head. She was being old-fashioned. Adrian was obviously trying to make the best of a difficult situation, and no doubt thought that an amicable—even slightly affectionate attitude between them—would help things along. He could suggest it because he did not care for her, but she loved him too much to maintain a lighthearted affection when she ached for something deeper.

CHAPTER TEN

IN the morning Tanya went to the library in the nearby town to look up some statistics for Adrian's secretary. Diana, who had some shopping to do there, drove her in.

As they bowled along in Diana's red coupé passers-by stared at them curiously, for the nine days' wonder of Tanya's identity had not yet died down. But as always, Diana was unselfconscious of the looks they aroused. It was as if she was determined to show she did not care about the gossip.

'Well?' Diana said in her cool voice. 'What conclusions have you come to about me?'

Tanya could not help smiling. 'Am I so obvious?'

'Let's say you'd not make a diplomat!'

'You like pretence, then?'

'It's often necessary. It isn't always good to say everything you're thinking. Sometimes the only way one can keep oneself happy is not to face facts.'

It was the longest speech Diana had made to her, and Tanya was sorry she could not agree with it. 'If you do not face facts, you are living a lie,' she said. 'And I have always considered you to be unafraid of the truth.'

'I wasn't talking about myself,' Diana said in surprise.

'I'm sorry. You spoke with such feeling that I thought you were.'

They drove for a while in silence, and again it was Diana who broke it.

'I suppose it's understandable that you should be

curious about me. After all, Adrian asked me to marry him. . . .'

'Yes,' Tanya said with composure. 'I would like to know what he found in you that he did not find in me.'

'I was here—and you weren't.'

'You are also very beautiful,' said Tanya, forcing out the words.

Diana made a disclaiming gesture. 'It has nothing to do with my looks. I think Adrian wanted his second marriage to be less demanding.'

'I never made demands on him,' Tanya said stiffly.

'I used the wrong word,' came the swift reply. 'I should have said less emotional.' The blue eyes were thoughtful. 'And you *are* emotional, Tanya. There's no point denying it.'

'I feel things deep down,' Tanya agreed, 'but I think you do also—deep down.'

'You do love analysing people, don't you?' Diana said lightly. 'It must by a mid-European habit!'

Tanya took this as a sign to discontinue the conversation and talk between them lapsed until they reached the little market town and parked near the main shopping precinct.

'How long will you be in the library?' Diana asked.

'A couple of hours.'

'Then let's meet at Procter's Coffee Shop about eleven-thirty.'

Tanya shook her head. 'The British weather I can bear, but the coffee we are served in the restaurants—never!'

Diana chuckled. 'Very well. I'll meet you back here.'

It was midday before they set off on the return journey, bowling along the country lanes so fast that the hedges merged into a blur of green. It was interesting that

Diana drove with such competence, and once again Tanya was sure there were greater depths to the girl than could be divined from a surface acquaintance with her.

'I'm not driving too fast for you, am I?' Diana asked.

'No, no. You are a good driver. You drive like a man.'

'I hope that's a compliment.'

'Of course. You are capable in everything you do. You never allow your emotions to walk away with you.'

'Run away with you,' Diana corrected. 'It's amusing when——' She stopped as the car gave a jerk. It travelled a few yards and then jerked again before slowing down to a stop. Diana turned off the ignition and then switched it on again, but the engine refused to turn over, and after fiddling with the choke, she slid out of the seat and walked round to the front to peer into the bonnet.

Tanya clambered out too. 'Do you know what is wrong?'

'I'm afraid not.' Diana bent further over the engine, emerging again with her hair over her eyes and an oily smut on her nose. 'I can't see anything loose, and all the leads seem to be plugged in properly.'

'Perhaps there is no petrol?'

'The gauge showed full when I left home.' She went back to the driving seat and switched on the engine. 'You're right,' she called. 'The gauge is still showing full—which it shouldn't do because I've used a couple of gallons this morning. It looks as if we'll be stuck here till I can get some more petrol. I'll walk back to the garage. There's one by the crossroads.'

'I'll go,' Tanya volunteered. 'It is better if you remain with the car.'

As Tanya set off, Diana closed the bonnet and, deciding it was too hot to sit in the car, leaned against the door and raised her face to the sun, closing her eyes at the same time.

'A funny place to have a doze,' a voice said behind her.

It was a voice that had haunted her dreams and she straightened up quickly and looked at Roger.

'I've run out of petrol,' she said coldly, and waited for him to laugh. Instead he looked sympathetic.

'Broken gauge, I suppose?'

Gratified that he had not—like many men would have done in similar circumstances— assumed she had forgotten to fill the tank, she nodded.

'I'll go along to the nearest garage and get you some,' he volunteered.

'Tanya's gone.'

'In that case I'll keep you company until she comes back.'

'You needn't bother, thank you. I'm quite happy on my own.'

'On your own and untouched.'

Furiously Diana turned her back on him. Hardly had she done so when he pulled her round and, expecting to see him angry, was surprised to see perplexity.

'Why do we always quarrel, Diana? We never used to in the old days.'

'When you were a boy you were always polite.'

'I can't remain a boy for ever,' he said thickly, and with rough strength pulled her against his chest and pressed his mouth upon hers.

There was no tenderness in his kiss, only passion, and she struggled to free herself. But he held her more tightly and made it impossible for her to move.

'Don't fight me,' he said huskily. 'I'm too strong for you.'

'Is that the only way you can get your women—by force?'

'It's the only way I can get *you*.' His mouth lowered to

hers once more. 'Kiss me back and I'll let you go,' he breathed. 'Until you do, you'll remain my prisoner.'

Knowing he was capable of doing as he said, she raised her head and closed her eyes, the movement of her lids clearly telling him to get his embrace over and done with.

'Oh no,' he said. 'Not like that! I want you to know who's kissing you.'

Her lids lifted sharply. 'Do you think I need to open my eyes to know that?' she snapped.

'Maybe not,' he said, once more capturing her mouth.

Because she had given her promise not to resist him, she remained motionless and the firm grip of his arms relaxed. But they did not move away from her and one hand slid gently round her waist while the other caressed the swelling curve of her breasts. She trembled, but knew it was not with revulsion. Her body was not under her control and muscles moved of their own accord as she responded to him. Again and again they kissed, their kisses deepening as their desire intensified. Diana had never known what it was to be wanted in such a wild and abandoned fashion, nor guessed she was so wildly capable of abandoning herself to it. Her hands were inside his sweater, her fingers on the smooth flesh of his chest and the fine tangle of hairs that lay there. His body was hot to her touch and knowing she was the cause of it, she was roused to an even greater desire.

It was only the sound of a distant car that made them aware of their surroundings, and Roger lifted his mouth from hers although he made no attempt to let her go.

'It isn't only in conversation that we strike sparks off each other,' he whispered.

'Don't read more into it than is there.' Diana's voice was thin, but she was relieved that she had at least managed to speak sanely when every part of her still insanely wanted to be held close to him. 'You're an attractive man and——'

'Don't tell me that's all it was. You aren't the type to be turned on by pressing the right button! You want me to make love to you. *Me!*'

'You fancy yourself, don't you?'

'You fancy me too.'

For answer her hand shot out and slapped him across the face. The sound was sharp, but no sharper than the look in his eyes as he stepped back, the mark of her fingers on his cheek.

'I thought you said smacking a man's face was reminiscent of cheap novels?'

'Maybe a cheap man can only understand a cheap gesture,' she said icily, and watched without expression as he turned on his heel and strode away.

Trembling, she climbed into the car and rested her head on the wheel, remaining there until steps behind her told her Tanya was back.

One look at Diana's face told Tanya something had happened to the girl in her absence. She had no need to ask what, for she had met Roger on her way back and the lipstick mark on his mouth was now giving her the answer. Silently she watched Diana pour in the petrol, then they returned to the car and headed towards Park Gates.

'I saw Roger,' Tanya commented.

'So did I. He—he offered to get me some petrol.'

Tanya waited and then, when no further information was forthcoming, said abruptly: 'I know you will think it very mid-European of me to ask such a question, but—do you love Adrian?'

There was a lengthy pause before Diana said coldly, 'Of course. I agreed to marry him.'

'Perhaps the word I should have used was passion. Do you feel passion for him?'

'Really, Tanya!' Diana made no attempt to hide her irritation. 'I'd rather we didn't continue this conversation. You're still his wife, you know.'

'In a few weeks he will be free to marry you and——'

'Please don't say any more.' A rabbit scuttled across the lane and Diana put her foot hard on the brake.

Tanya had forgotten to do up her safety belt and her head narrowly missed hitting the windscreen.

'Sorry about that,' Diana said swiftly. 'I didn't want to kill the poor thing.'

They continued to drive in silence and Tanya looked at the girl beside her, noticing the dishevelled hair and the mouth that was still trembling.

'I am longing to put my feet in it again,' she murmured, 'and tell you that I think Roger is in love with you.'

'Tanya!' Diana's voice rose high. 'Will you please be quiet? Roger and I mean nothing to each other. He and Adrian have been a part of my life for as long as I can remember, but it's Adrian I'm going to marry. Now if you don't want me to stop the car and let you walk the rest of the way, I suggest you change the conversation.'

'We will talk about the weather, then,' Tanya replied. 'On that subject we are sure to agree.'

For the next couple of days Diana avoided being alone with Tanya, but gradually their casual friendship was resumed and Diana, as if wanting to show she bore no resentment, was unexpectedly forthcoming about herself and her past. Her childhood had not been an easy one, for when her mother had died she had been sent to boarding school and, even when home for the holidays, had been looked after by an assortment of governesses.

'You had a great deal of attention,' Tanya commented one afternoon, 'but only a little affection.'

'My father isn't a demonstrative man,' said Diana. 'But he feels things deeply. He takes great pride in his heritage and—and the family as a whole. For many years he used to visit all our relatives, no matter where they lived.'

'Who will inherit the title?'

'A cousin in Scotland.'

'I suppose he must have minded very much that you weren't a boy,' Tanya said.

'I minded it too.' Diana picked up a pile of leaflets from the desk. 'I'm supposed to start canvassing at five. I'd better go down to party headquarters.'

'Better you than me.' Tanya knew Diana had plenty of time and was merely using her appointment as a means of ending the conversation. 'I would hate having to knock on doors and talk to strange people.'

'It isn't so bad talking to them,' Diana replied. 'It's having the door slammed in your face!'

Tanya was still smiling at this as Diana went out but, once alone, she thought over all the girl had said. Had Diana really wanted to be born a boy, and was this the reason she hid her undoubted warmth behind an air of coolness? She had not yet met Lord Biddell but knew he was a cantankerous man, made more so by his ill-health.

She was still wondering about Diana when Mrs Chesterton came in.

'There you are, Tanya,' the woman said so graciously that Tanya wondered whether she—like her son—was beginning to think it might be a good idea for the marriage to continue, at least until Adrian's political career was stabilised.

'I've just been talking to Lord Biddell,' Mrs Chesterton continued. 'He's been having treatment in Harrogate and only returned home last night. He's asked us to dine with him tomorrow.'

Tanya digested this. 'Does the invitation include me?'

'Naturally. You are Adrian's wife.'

'Diana also happens to be his fiancée.'

Mrs Chesterton gave a faintly embarrassed laugh. 'For the moment you are Adrian's wife and we all—we all expect you to be treated as such.'

'I do not think I would like to dine with Lord Biddell.'

'Don't be foolish, child. He's an important man and for Adrian's sake you must——'

'Very well,' Tanya interposed. 'Then I will come.'

'Wear one of your long dresses, my dear. And in one of those mauvy colours you like so much. They suit you so well.'

'Do you want Lord Biddell to see that Adrian has always had good taste?' Tanya asked.

'Well, he has, hasn't he?' On that parting shot Mrs Chesterton retired.

Tanya half expected Adrian to make some comment to her about their forthcoming meeting with Lord Biddell. But that night he left the house early to speak at a meeting in one of the outlying villages some distance away, and even the next day he did not refer to it. Deciding that if he was not embarrassed to take along a wife to meet the man whom he had hoped—and no doubt still hoped—would be his father-in-law then she herself was not going to be embarrassed either.

That evening she dressed with great care, and gazing at herself in the cheval mirror was more than satisfied with her appearance. One of the first results of her official recognition as Adrian's wife had been an enlargement of her wardrobe, and her protests at its luxuriousness had been quickly quenched by Mrs Chesterton's statement that Adrian's wife could no longer look like a Rovnian refugee.

Well, no one could mistake her for a refugee tonight. The flowing skirt in amethyst silk gave height to her slender figure, encircling her waist tightly and then falling to the ground in deep pleats. With it she wore an organdie blouse of blush pink with a wide shawl collar and full sleeves. It was a look that suited her personality, being a combination of virginality and sexuality.

There was no one in the drawing-room when she entered it and she wandered across to look at the garden. Almost at once she saw Adrian by the balustrade, but before she could draw back he turned and saw her.

'I'm glad you're down early. I want to talk to you.' He walked in through the french windows, his blue eyes narrowing as he saw the lovely picture she made. 'I like you in that dress. I haven't seen it before.'

'Your mother bought it for me last week.'

'You're the type for flowing skirts and graceful fabrics. You should never wear anything slinky.'

'The slinky look is out of fashion anyway,' she said, refusing to see his remark as a compliment.

'A beautiful woman can make her own fashion,' he replied, and hands in the pockets of his dinner jacket, went on surveying her.

Resolutely Tanya refused to let herself be swayed by his regard. But though she kept her eyes focused on his face, she was intensely aware of everything about him; the wide shoulders that tapered down to a narrow waist and lithe hips; the haughty tilt of his head that was belied by the sensitive curve of his mouth; the hard line of his cheekbone that was at direct variance with the

tender way his narrow white hands—one of which had
now come out to stroke the side of his face—had held
and caressed her. But it was madness to see him so
intimately and she wished she could as easily control her
imagination as she was now able to control her tongue.

'It's about Diana's father,' said Adrian, breaking into
her thoughts. 'He knows about you and——'

'If you'd rather I didn't come with you, I won't mind.'

'Of course you must come with me. You're my wife.'

'Not really.'

'That's another thing I want to talk about. I've tried
not to say anything before, but——'

Whatever it was he had tried not to say, Tanya was
never to find out, for her mother-in-law sailed regally in,
at full mast in ruby brocade, followed almost at once by
Betty and Dick, bringing up the rear like a couple of
frigates.

Ten minutes later Tanya found herself in Lord Biddell's home. It was a large Queen Anne house, whose
dignified exterior was echoed by its even more dignified
furnishings. Looking round the sombre panelled hall and
the stiffly elegant drawing-room, she began to understand a little of what went to make up Diana's character.
How true it was that one never knew a person until one
had seen them in their own home or lived with them, she
thought as the girl, elegant in black, came forward to
greet them.

But if Diana fitted into her background, her father did
not, being stocky and broad, with a ruddy complexion
and thick features that looked as though they had been
hewn out of wood: teak at the very least. His eyes were
the same colour as his daughter's but had a much more
piercing quality, and as they stared at Tanya, she felt as
though they were looking right through her.

'I can see why Adrian married you,' he grunted. 'You're a good-looking filly.'

In the awkward silence that followed—during which he seemed the only person to be unembarrassed—he busied himself at a tray of drinks, muttering angrily when he could not find the ice.

'I swear I'll sack Tomkins if he doesn't mend his ways.' He turned to his daughter. 'Get some ice at once!'

Quickly Diana went from the room and Tanya looked at her host in amazement. Did he always speak to his daughter in that way, and did she always comply so meekly? No one else seemed to notice anything strange and she wondered if she were being unduly sensitive. But as the evening continued, she decided she was not, for the man continually treated his daughter as if she were a child. Not only did he order her to do this and that as a matter of course, but he continually interrupted her when she was speaking and once, when she made as though to interrupt *him*, he raised a hand and ordered her to be quiet.

Inevitably the talk came round to the by-election.

'You've nothing to worry about, my boy,' Lord Biddell said heartily. 'The country people have still got enough sense to vote for you and not that bounder Poulton.'

Quickly Tanya looked at Diana, but the girl went on eating composedly.

But Tanya was made of sterner stuff and she set down her fork and addressed her host. 'Why do you call Mr Poulton a bounder?'

'Because he is. I'd like to boot him and his family out of the country.'

Tanya lost her temper. 'Have you forgotten that Roger's father fought for his country and died in Ireland—or do these things not count any more?'

'Of course they count.' Lord Biddell went on cutting his meat imperturbably. 'I didn't say the family were cowards. I merely said they should be turfed out.'

'Because they don't hold the same views as you?'

Only then did Lord Biddell take note of her comments and he fixed her with a steely look. 'You shouldn't go round defending your husband's opponent, my gel. Not good form, you know.'

'In my country it is not considered good form to run down a man when he is not present to defend himself!'

There was an audible gasp from Mrs Chesterton and the two younger women kept their eyes fixed on their plates. Only Adrian stared directly at Tanya, the hand holding the stem of his wine glass so tightly clenched that the fingers were white. But when he spoke his voice was calm.

'Lord Biddell doesn't always mean precisely what he says. When you get to know him better you will realise that for yourself.'

'Adrian's right,' the older man chuckled. 'I always express my opinions strongly. It's the only thing I *can* be strong about!'

The awkward moment passed and Tanya vowed to guard her impetuousness.

Dinner over, the men remained at the table with their port while Mrs Chesterton and Betty retired to powder their faces, leaving Diana and Tanya alone in the drawing-room.

'I hope Father didn't upset you?' Diana murmured.

'I did not mind what he said,' Tanya replied, 'so much as I minded that you did not come to Roger's defence.'

'Why should I? If you're still persisting in that ridiculous idea that I love him——'

'Let us leave love out of it. Let us remember only that you are his friend.'

'I don't think Roger and I *are* friends any more,' Diana said flatly.

'Is that why you allowed him to kiss you the day the car broke down?'

'I couldn't help it. He forced me. He's always doing things like that.'

'So! He is always doing things like that! Yet you still pretend you do not know he loves you?'

For an instant Diana was lost for words, then her native intelligence came to her aid. 'You said yourself that love has nothing to do with passion. And that's all Roger feels for me—passion.'

'And love,' Tanya added.

'No! He's a virile man and if a girl appeals to him he——'

'What nonsense are you talking? You cannot believe Roger goes around kissing all the attractive women he sees? No matter what you say you are not so stupid as to think that! Or are you too much of a snob to admit what you feel for him?'

'I don't feel anything for him!' Diana jumped up from her chair and walked to the far end of the room, where she made a pretence of straightening some cushions. Without turning round she spoke. 'I have no feelings towards Roger and I wish you would stop saying so. Otherwise I'll begin to think you're deliberately trying to create a romance between us in order to get Adrian for yourself!'

Tanya shrank back visibly, but refused to concede she was wrong. 'I would never do anything to win Adrian back and whatever I have said about Roger, I truly mean. Maybe you do not love him—I will not argue about that any longer—but he loves *you*. Of that I am positive.'

Diana's lips parted, but before she could speak Mrs Chesterton and Betty came in, followed by the men. Lord Biddell was in excellent humour and suggested a game of bridge.

He looked at Tanya. 'Do you play?'

'I'm afraid not.'

'Then Diana and I will take on Adrian and Mrs Chesterton. Betty and Dick are only beginners.'

'I'd rather not play tonight,' Diana intervened. 'I have a headache.'

'It will do you good to play.'

'I don't want to.'

Lord Biddell's hearty colour deepened and Betty created a diversion by pulling the chairs into position round the bridge table and suggesting that she herself took Diana's place. 'Do let me play,' she said brightly. 'My bridge has improved no end.'

Soon a game was in progress, while Diana and Dick sat with Tanya on the far side of the room and tried to teach her how to play gin rummy. But Tanya could not keep her mind on the cards. She had not failed to notice Diana's attempt to stand up to her father and, weak though the rebellion had been, she wondered if there was some significance in it.

'Keep your mind on the game, Tanya,' Dick said jovially. 'You've been blitzed on two columns already.'

Smiling her apology, Tanya concentrated on her cards, but soon her thoughts wandered again, this time to Adrian. How well he fitted into this stately home! He treated Lord Biddell with exactly the right amount of deference and good humour, and would make him an admirable son-in-law; as Lord Biddell—with his immense wealth and illustrious name—would make him an admirable father-in-law. Yes, Adrian and Diana were destined to marry and neither she nor Roger would be able to stop it.

On this miserable thought she determinedly concentrated on the cards in her hand, marvelling at her ability to pretend interest when all she wanted to do was to run away and hide.

CHAPTER ELEVEN

IT was not often that Roger was irritated by his family. For as long as he could remember he had been used to working with people swarming around him and had learned not to allow them to affect his concentration. But tonight the ceaseless chatter of his brothers and sisters worked on his strung-up nerves until it was all he could do not to box Brian's ears, the noisiest and most energetic of them all.

Fortunately Mrs Poulton could always tell when things were getting too much for her eldest son and, with a few sharp words, succeeded in getting the living-room cleared. Then she lowered the volume on the radio, poured out another cup of tea and pushed it across the table.

'Drink it while it's hot,' she advised. 'It will do you good.'

Roger smiled wryly and obeyed.

'Had a bad day, son?'

'I've known better. Adrian's putting up a good fight. It'll be touch and go.'

'I still think you'll win.'

'Spoken like a mother!' The doorbell rang and he groaned. 'I don't want to see anyone tonight. Answer it for me and make some excuse, will you?'

Obediently she rose, but when she returned to the living-room she was not alone, and Roger, seeing the girl with her, jumped quickly to his feet.

'What are *you* doing here?' he said harshly.

'Roger!' Mrs Poulton spoke before Diana could do so. 'What a way to to talk to a visitor!' She looked at the girl. 'Don't take any notice of him. He's tired.'

'Don't find excuses for my ill humour, Mother,' Roger said sourly. 'I'm sure Diana doesn't expect me to be polite.'

Mrs Poulton went out again, closing the door behind her, and Roger motioned Diana to a chair. 'Mother's right,' he said hesitantly. 'I'm pretty vile-tempered when I've been overdoing it. Sorry.'

'That's all right. As a matter of fact I'm the one who owes you an apology. That's why I came.'

'An apology for what?'

'For—for smacking your face the other day.'

Roger was momentarily taken aback, then he smiled. 'I think I asked for it.'

'I know you did,' she said coldly. 'But one ill-advised action doesn't deserve another.'

'Did you say you'd come here to apologise?' he asked with gentle sarcasm.

'Yes. But you always rub me up the wrong way and make me lose my temper again.'

'At least it shows you're human.' He swung a chair round and sat astride it, facing her. 'Until you hit me the other day, I'd always thought of you as being as calm as the Sphinx.'

'Is it wrong to be calm?'

'Only if there's a danger of it becoming stagnation.'

She caught her breath. 'You don't mince *your* words, do you?'

'That's my trouble—I speak before I think.'

'It's a habit you should learn to control. Otherwise it will affect your career.'

'How right you are,' he mocked. 'Maybe I need a wife

who can cure me of my bad habits and turn me into a
gentleman. Would you care to take on the job?'

'I'd fail at it,' she answered. 'One has to have the
potential to work on.'

'You don't mince words either,' he remarked, rocking
backwards and forwards on his chair. 'That blow was
very much below the belt.'

'I don't think either of us worry where we aim our
blows. All our conversations degenerate into slanging
matches.'

'It's as much my fault as yours,' he said magnani-
mously. 'Stay a bit longer and have a cup of tea—just to
prove we can talk without riling each other.'

'I can't stay,' said Diana. 'Father's expecting me back
for a drink before dinner.'

Roger's eyebrows rose and his temper with it. 'Ever
thought of disobeying him? Or are you too scared?'

'Scared of what?'

'Standing on your own two feet?'

'If I wanted to stand on my own, I could do so. But it
so happens I prefer to give in to my father.'

'Why?'

'Because I owe it to him.'

'Owe it to him?' Roger was perplexed. 'What do you
owe him?'

'Obedience and——' she hesitated. 'Obedience and
love. I'm all he has,' she went on. 'If there'd been other
children . . . if he'd had a son . . .'

'My God, you sound like a psychologist's casebook!'
Roger's tone was disbelieving. 'Don't tell me you've got
a guilt complex because you weren't born a man?'

'Is that so hard for you to understand? Can't you
imagine how he felt when he learned my mother couldn't
have any more children after I was born? He was des-

perate for a son—to have his own child inherit the title.'

'The title won't die out,' said Roger, still looking bemused. 'I can't get over you feeling like this. It's so—so anachronistic.'

'Because you've been brought up to a different sort of life—but to me it seems logical.'

'Not logical,' he corrected. 'Emotional.'

'At least you admit I'm capable of having emotions.'

His eyes rested on her mouth and she knew instantly that he was remembering the way she had responded to his kisses. For a brief moment she looked at him, seeing how tired he was, how pale and lined his face. Had his hair always been so unruly—that wild mop of red through which she longed to run her fingers?

Abruptly she checked her thoughts, regretting the impulse that had brought her here. It was Tanya's fault. Tanya who was trying to make her fall in love with someone other than Adrian. Yet she had never loved Adrian. He had never been able to arouse her the way Roger did. Her heart was pounding and she was afraid he would see the pulse that throbbed in her throat.

'I must go,' she whispered.

Silently he went to her car. 'Haven't you ever wanted to fight for something you believed in?' he asked as she got into the front seat.

'Not until now.'

'That sounds interesting. Care to tell me what it is?'

'My own freedom,' she replied slowly. 'The right to do exactly as I want.'

There was such sadness in her eyes that Roger knew a strong urge to pull her out of the car and into his arms. The effort not to do so made his voice harsh with strain.

'If you really wanted your freedom, you could get it.'

'Regardless of how one hurts others?'

'You can't make an omelette without breaking eggs.'

'I hate omelettes,' she cried, and viciously pressed the starter and drove away.

With a sense of futility—an attitude that rarely afflicted him—Roger went to his bedroom; the one place where he knew he would be undisturbed. Seeing Diana was becoming more and more of a torment to him and he rued the day when he had first kissed her. Even now he did not know what had prompted him to do it. But seeing her walking towards him in the woods, slender and cool as the young spring trees burgeoning into life around her, he had been overwhelmed by the self-same emotions she had aroused in him when he had been in his late teens. How surprised she would be to know that even when a youth he had been head over heels in love with her.

'But not now,' he muttered aloud. 'I've better things to do than waste my life wanting a woman who's scared to admit she even likes me!'

Flinging back his shoulders in a fighting gesture which his political agent would have been delighted to see, he strode down to his office. There was work to be done, and in his work he would find peace.

Tanya was on her way to the village the next morning when she saw Roger coming out of the Post Office. They had not met since the night she had called at his house to tell him her identity had been discovered, and she was wondering whether to avoid him when he caught sight of her and came over. Close up he looked tired; his face set in lines of worry, his hands restlessly fidgeting with the sheaf of papers in his hands.

'Long time no see,' he said.

'I've been very busy.'

'Making sure Adrian wins?' She coloured and he touched her arm. 'Sorry, Tanya, I didn't mean that. Come and have a coffee with me?'

'Do you think we should be seen together?'

'What the hell? Friends are more important than politics!'

Nodding, she followed him to the café where they had gone before, and when the usual pale grey liquid that passed for coffee had been set in front of them, she studied his face again.

'You are not looking well, Roger. Is it because of Diana?'

'What does she have to do with it?'

'You are in love with her. I——'

'For God's sake!' he burst out. 'Are you running an agony column?'

'You and Diana are making your own agony.'

'Don't tell me you spout this rot to her?' Roger was looking furious. 'Damn it, Tanya, you've got to stop interfering in other people's lives.'

'Very well.' Her eyes were wide, unblinking. 'Go on with your pretence. You *and* Diana. Life is so short and meaningless that it doesn't matter if you play act your way through it.'

'Don't!' His voice was anguished. 'You know I don't believe that. But...' He shook his head. What was the use of fighting his feelings any more? Of course he loved Diana; he would love her for the rest of his life.

'You're right,' he muttered. 'But where will it get me? We'd never be happy together.'

Tears glittered in Tanya's beautiful eyes. 'You must try. Diana loves you too. She's never admitted it to me, but I know she does.'

'You're wrong. She's too much her father's daughter. And even if she liked me. . . .'

'She loves you.'

'She loves her father more.'

'As much, perhaps,' Tanya conceded. 'But not more. That's why you must show her the way.'

'Show her the way?'

'Tell her how you feel.'

'She'd still never do anything to upset her father.'

'Have you asked her to marry you?'

'Don't be crazy!' he snapped.

'Then how do you expect her to break away from him? Or are you waiting for her to propose to *you*?'

'You're trying to make me look a fool,' Roger said curtly. 'And you know as well as I do that unless Diana stands up to her father we wouldn't have a chance of being happy together.'

'You must give her a reason to stand up to him,' Tanya said.

'I've no intention of making the first move.'

Tanya flung her hands in the air. 'You are stubborn, like a donkey! You must make the first move—she must make the first move—never have I heard so many moves with everybody standing still!' She leaned close to him. 'If you will give Diana some encouragement—enough to show her she is in your thoughts—I'm convinced she will find her courage.'

'I can't tell her,' he stated. 'If you're wrong. . . . No, it's out of the question. She'd laugh in my face.'

'Poor little boy,' Tanya mocked with the first cruelty she had ever shown to him. 'I did not realise you were so afraid.'

The colour in his face rivalled his hair. 'Leave it,' he said tersely.

She nodded. 'I will leave the coffee also. It is too weak.'

'Like me.' Roger tossed some coins on the table and followed her from the café.

'Are we still friends?' she asked, her voice wobbly.

Without hesitation he gripped her shoulders. 'Yes, always, Tanya. Always.'

CHAPTER TWELVE

'DIANA, where are you?'

Lord Biddell's voice boomed along the hall and the huge antlers on the head of a slaughtered stag decorating one wall appeared to quiver with the sound.

Diana turned from the front door. 'What is it, Father?'

'Come into the library. I want to talk to you.'

'I'm on my way out. Won't it do later?'

'No, it won't,' her father shouted back. 'Come here!'

With a shrug, she obeyed him and found him sitting behind his massive oak desk, a cigar in his mouth, his ruddy face looking as though nothing in the world could startle it out of its lines of self-satisfaction.

'I hear you've been going around with that Poulton chap,' he began abruptly. 'Is it true?'

'No, it isn't.'

'Somebody saw you coming out of his house.'

'I went to see him,' she replied. 'But that hardly constitutes going out with him.'

'Well, whatever it constitutes, I won't have it. Do you hear?'

'I can hardly avoid hearing. Not when you're bellowing at me like this.'

Her father looked startled. 'What's up with you, gel? In the last few weeks you've changed.'

'Maybe I'm growing up,' she shrugged.

'Growing up! What nonsense are you talking? You're already grown up!'

'I'm surprised you realise it.'

'Don't be clever with me,' he growled. 'If I——' He stopped as the housekeeper entered, carrying a large bouquet of long-stemmed roses and a mass of violets. 'What the devil's that?'

'They're for Miss Diana, sir,' the woman replied.

Looking as surprised as her father, Diana took the flowers and from an envelope attached to the paper extracted a card.

'Don't be like the violets that grow best when in the shade,' she read, 'but be like the roses that open themselves wide to the warmth of the sun.' Below the message was Roger's scrawled signature, and colour stained her cheeks as she quickly made for the door.

'Who are they from?' her father called after her.

'Roger Poulton.'

'What the devil does he mean by sending you flowers?'

'Why shouldn't he? He's a friend of mine.'

'You haven't seen him for years,' Lord Biddell growled. 'It's that foreign gel who's made you think like this—Adrian's wife. I always knew no good would come out of that marriage.'

'Why shouldn't I be friends with Roger?' Diana exploded. 'I've known him for years and he's exceptionally clever.'

'I'll grant you he's clever. I've heard one or two of his speeches and he knows how to get his point across—even if it's the wrong one. But cleverness isn't everything, my gel, and you've got to stop seeing him.'

'I'm not seeing him.'

'You went to his house.'

'Because I ...' There was no way Diana could bring herself to tell her father the real reason and instead she

was forced to lie. 'I used to go there when I was a child
and—and I wanted to see him again.'

'What for? You're not a child now. You're a woman,
and you should behave like one.'

'I would if you treated me like one! Unfortunately
you've always treated me as if I were a child; telling me
what to do, what to wear, whom to see.' Her voice was
choked with tears. 'Even whom I should marry.'

'And a fine mess that turned out to be,' her father
barked. 'I've an idea Adrian's fallen for that wife of his.'

'Good luck to him if he has! He'd be crazy if he sent
her away.'

'Now I know you're mad,' her father grunted.

'Why? Because I've no intention of marrying Adrian?'

'Because of Poulton!' her father roared. 'Don't tell me
that bounder means anything to you?'

'He means everything!' Diana was so angry she was
hardly aware of what she was saying. 'And don't call
him a bounder! I love him, do you hear? I love him!'

There was a long silence and it was difficult to know
who was more astonished: Diana or her father. But her
father found his composure first and when he spoke, he
did so almost gently.

'Do you know what you're saying, Diana?'

'I—er—I didn't. Not until I actually said it,' she
whispered. 'Until now I—I didn't even know it was true.'

'Of course it isn't true!' Lord Biddell leant back in his
chair and tried to look avuncular. 'You're overwrought,
my gel. It's all this business of Adrian that's upset you.
And naturally you've got pride and you don't want to
admit you're hurt.'

'I'm not hurt because of Adrian. I wouldn't marry him
even if he were free. I don't love him—I never did.'

'Maybe you do, maybe you don't. That's neither here nor there for the moment. Right now I'm concerned to get you on an even keel again. Perhaps you should take a cruise? Go to America or the Bahamas. You'll feel a different person when you've had a change of scene.'

'I already feel a different person. And for the first time in my life I know what I want without you telling me.'

'I've only wanted what was best for you,' her father said. 'You're like a son to me and——'

'No, Father! I'm not a son and I never can be. That's always been the trouble. I've tried to be the son you never had and because of it, I've failed to be a woman. We've both been fooling ourselves, and we've got to stop. I can't carry your name for ever, and even if I gave you a grandson he wouldn't carry it either.'

Lord Biddell's face darkened. 'I suppose you expect me to welcome a grandson with the name of Poulton?'

It was a moment before Diana replied. 'I've never thought of it until now, but ... but why not?'

'Does the fellow love you?' her father asked abruptly.

'Why should he? I've never given him any encouragement.'

'Men like him don't need encouragement.' Her father saw the flash in her eyes and said quickly: 'At least he's got more sense than you! He knows his place even if you don't!'

'We've all got a place in the world,' she said furiously, 'and you're no more important in it than anyone else.'

Not giving her father a chance to reply, she flung open the door and ran out. Dropping the bouquet on to one of the tables in the hall, she raced out of the house. She had been going to the Post Office when her father had asked to see her, but she could no longer face meeting anyone in the village. Her mind in a turmoil, she sped through

the bushes to the drive, and only when she saw the gates
leading to Adrian's house did she realise she had come
in search of Tanya.

Tanya was the one person to whom she could talk
freely. Tanya was the only one who had realised the
truth of her feelings before she had realised them for
herself. Breathlessly she rounded a bend and saw the
house in front of her. Adrian's car was by the door and
he and Tanya were climbing into it.

'Hello there,' he called. 'I've a meeting in Little Compton. Care to come along?'

'I can't.' Diana reached the car and looked at Tanya.
'Are you going with Adrian?'

'Yes. Did you want to talk to me?'

'We can't stop now,' Adrian cut in. 'We're late already.'

'I'll telephone you when I get back,' said Tanya.

'I'm not sure I'll be home.' Diana made a vague
gesture with her hand. 'Perhaps it's best if I call you.'

She headed across the grass, taking the short cut she
generally used when coming over from her home. Tanya
watched until she had disappeared behind the shrubbery
and then turned to Adrian.

'I'm sure there's something wrong. Maybe I should
have stayed here and talked to her.'

'It's too late now. I'm sure it can wait.'

They drove to the meeting in silence, and only when
Tanya had taken her place on the dais behind Adrian
and saw the audience looking expectantly up at him was
she able to forget Diana and concentrate on her husband. He looked unusually pale and she knew he had
sensed the air of belligerency in the hall. She could sense
it too and knew the meeting was going to be a noisy one.

It was even worse than she had expected. Adrian was

only able to speak for a few minutes without inter-
ruption, then hecklers took over and he was shouted
down. He did his best to gain control, but as the shout-
ing grew worse he looked in Tanya's direction. She knew
he was waiting for her to signal him they should go, but
she was determined not to let him walk out on his critics.
If Adrian genuinely believed in what he was saying, he
must find the strength to make people listen to him.
Imperceptibly she shook her head, and he squared his
shoulders and turned back to face the audience.

The din continued, but he raised his voice above it and
gradually a few of his words could be heard. Some of the
people quietened and started to listen to him again, and
when a heckler shouted at him from the far end of the
hall, he turned what could have been a dangerous question into a joke against himself. From then on the
atmosphere changed and the meeting swung in his fav-
our.

When it was over the storm of applause made up for
the first bad quarter of an hour, and as they left the hall,
Adrian caught Tanya's arm.

'Thanks for making me stick it out. I wouldn't have
done if you hadn't been with me.'

It was the first positive acknowledgment he had made
to her that her presence had helped him, and she was
angry because she felt so warmed by it.

'I'm glad I can be of service to you,' she replied.

'Service is the wrong word to use.'

She did not answer, and Adrian took away his arm.
During their drive home he was once more aloof, answering her questions courteously but contributing nothing to the conversation himself. After a while Tanya
huddled silently in her seat. She was glad only two days
separated them from polling time. Once it was over she

would be free to go; free to tear Adrian out of her life and build a new one for herself.

There was still more than an hour to go before dinner when they entered the house, and Tanya paused in the hall. 'I think I'll go over to Diana.'

'If you'd mentioned it earlier, I could have dropped you off. Hang on a moment and I'll drive you there.'

'There's no need. A walk will do me good.'

Across the hall their eyes met. His were unsmiling and his lips were set in such a tight line that she thought he was going to lose his temper. Then with a shrug he turned his back on her and went into the library.

Refusing to think of him, Tanya headed for Diana's home. Only when she reached the imposing entrance did she know a momentary fear, though this evaporated as her ring brought a friendly-looking maid to the door.

'I'm afraid Miss Diana isn't at home,' the girl said to Tanya's query. 'His Lordship is waiting for her.'

'Is that you, Diana?' Tanya jumped nervously as Lord Biddell's voice boomed down the hall and the man himself came into view, leaning on a walking stick.

'Oh, it's Adrian's wife, is it? Come in, come in. I thought it was Diana.'

Tanya obeyed her host's instruction and followed him to the library.

'Can't think what's happened to the gel,' he said. 'It's well past my dinner-time and I've never known her be so late.'

'Do you know where she went?'

'No.' He frowned. 'Never known her behave like this. Shouted at me like a fishwife and then rushed out.'

'At least she's showing a little spirit,' Tanya said with daring.

'I suppose I owe that to you, eh?'

'I've never told your daughter how to behave.'

'But you've been showing her by example,' Lord Biddell grunted. 'Don't know what's coming over the world these days. Everyone's taken leave of their senses. You wouldn't care to have dinner with me instead, would you?'

'I'm afraid I can't. The family will be expecting me back.'

'Then you'd better go.' Lord Biddell accompanied her to the door. 'No point having everybody dine late!'

Tanya could not help smiling and he glared at her and then surprisingly smiled back.

'I wish Diana had your spirit.'

'A few minutes ago you said she had—and that you didn't like it!'

'I hate being reminded of what I said!' Lord Biddell answered abruptly. 'That's the trouble with women. They always remind you of what you've said!'

Tanya laughed outright. Taken in small doses Lord Biddell was amusing, but she could quite see why Diana had been intimidated by him and also why—though rather late in life—she had finally rebelled.

By the time she reached Park Gates the family were already at table and she slipped into her place next to Adrian—the position of hostess still being occupied by Mrs Chesterton. She was grateful when Adrian only briefly enquired if she had seen Diana and did not pursue the subject until, dinner over and the family heading towards the drawing-room and coffee, he slowed his steps and made it clear he wished to talk with her alone.

'I gather you didn't manage to speak to Diana?'

'She wasn't at home and her father didn't know where she was.'

'Do you think they've quarrelled?'

'I'm sure of it. I wish I hadn't gone with you to the meeting. I knew she wanted to talk to me about something important and I should have stayed and listened to her.'

'It's pointless to feel guilty about it,' he said. 'Anyway, I think you're worrying for nothing.'

'I don't.'

'She isn't the type to do anything silly,' Adrian said quickly. 'She's probably annoyed with herself for losing her temper and has gone off somewhere to cool down. I'm sure she'll return home later this evening.'

There was logic in what Adrian had said and she nodded. 'I suppose you're right.'

'That's the first time you've admitted I could be right about anything.'

The words were humorous, but there was no humour in Adrian's voice, only a bitterness which Tanya could not understand. What right did he have to be bitter when she was the one who had been wronged?

'I won't have any coffee,' she said flatly. 'I would prefer to go to my room.'

He walked with her to the foot of the stairs. 'I won't always let you run away from me, Tanya. We have things to talk about, but I'll leave it until after the election.'

She nodded and went up the stairs. She had no intention of having any discussion with Adrian, either before or after the election. But to say no would precipitate an argument and she was already at the end of her tether. Once she was no longer required to remain here, she would pack her bags and run.

CHAPTER THIRTEEN

BRIGHT sunlight shining through a chink in the curtains awakened Tanya the next morning. Memory returned instantly and she donned her dressing-gown and ran downstairs to telephone Lord Biddell. But Diana had not returned home, nor had there been word from her.

'Have you contacted the police?' Tanya asked hesitantly.

'No!' It was an angry sound. 'She rushed out of the house like a bad-tempered filly and she'll be back as soon as she's cooled off. I know my daughter.'

Tanya forbore to say that by Lord Biddell's own account, Diana had never behaved in such a fashion before. Determinedly she tried to sow a seed of fear in his mind that might grow and precipitate him into taking some action if Diana did not return that day.

'She may have had an accident or been taken ill. Perhaps if you called the police....'

'If she'd had an accident I'd have heard about it soon enough,' Lord Biddell said testily. 'As for her being ill ... she's never had a day's illness in her life. And I certainly don't want to bring in the police. Never heard such twaddle!'

Tanya replaced the receiver, all her anxiety for Diana —which Adrian had helped to diminish last night— returning in full force. Diana must have gone *somewhere*. She couldn't be wandering round the countryside like a lost sheep.

She was halfway up the stairs when she thought of

Roger. Could Diana have gone to him? It was not the
sort of action the girl would normally take, but then she
had been far from normal yesterday. Quickly Tanya ran
downstairs again, stopping on the last step as Adrian
came out of the breakfast room. Only the slight raising
of his eyebrows gave away his surprise at seeing her in a
state of déshabille. Until this morning she had never left
her bedroom without being fully dressed.

'You're just in time to join me for breakfast,' he said.

'I haven't come down for breakfast. I want to phone
Roger.'

'What for?'

'In case Diana's there. She might have gone to him.'

Only when the words were out did Tanya realise that
until this moment she had never given Adrian an inkling
of how Roger and Diana felt about each other. With this
knowledge came the more unpleasant one that Adrian
might well think she had deliberately fostered a romance
between the two in order to get Diana out of the way.

'Are you telling me Diana and Poulton are in love
with one another?' Adrian demanded.

'I know Roger loves Diana,' Tanya replied, 'and I'm
almost sure she feels the same way.'

'Has she said so?'

'Not in actual words, but ... but ... they're feelings
Diana has tried to hide. That's why I wanted to ring
Roger.'

'If Diana's tried to hide her feelings, you should respect them,' Adrian said coldly. 'And if she were with
Poulton and wanted you to know she'd have called you
herself.'

'Then what should I do?'

'Nothing—for the moment. Have some breakfast first
and then we'll think again.'

The warmth of his hand on her arm penetrated the silk of her dressing-gown and she longed to throw herself against him and feel the strength of his hold. Instead she pulled sharply away from him and walked into the breakfast-room. Silently she watched as he poured her a cup of coffee, carefully cut and buttered a roll and put it on a plate.

'Eat up,' he counselled gently. 'It will help you to feel better. How long have you known?'

'Known what?'

'That they're—that they were in love?'

'I've suspected it for some time. Diana's still fighting it, but Roger admitted it a little while ago.'

Adrian sat down and regarded her intently, his expression sad. 'Poor Tanya, you haven't been lucky in love, have you? You mustn't...'

'I was never in love with Roger,' she cut across him, determined not to have his sympathy. 'He was—he still is—my friend. Nothing more.'

Adrian's look clearly showed he did not believe her and her determination grew.

'I'm not interested in marrying anyone else for the moment. And when I do, it won't be someone who will remind me of my association with you!'

The rise of colour that washed Adrian's features told Tanya she had succeeded in convincing him she did not love Roger and, equally important, that she did not love *him* either.

'To return to Diana,' he said tonelessly. 'If she loves Poulton—as you say—she may well have gone away for a few days in order to think things out.'

Tanya allowed Adrian's words to comfort her, but later that morning, when he had left the house with Dick to inspect a couple of home farms, her earlier fears returned. It was true Diana was sensible, but when a woman was overwrought and believed she loved but was unloved in return, she might do something silly.

On an impulse she picked up the phone to call Roger, and had half dialled his number when she put down the receiver. To ask him bluntly if Diana was with him might not be the most tactful thing to do, whereas if she went to see him she might be able to find out.

She was breathless from running by the time she reached Roger's house and she paused for a moment to catch her breath. The one thing she did not want was to arrive here looking anxious. There was a sound of activity behind the door and, afraid it would open and her presence be discovered, she quickly knocked.

The door was opened by Roger. He looked startled, as well he might, for Tanya had never called on him since taking over her role as Adrian's wife. Then he recovered himself and smiled.

'What a lovely surprise! I take it it's a social visit?'

'Yes.' Her voice was low. 'May I come in?'

'Of course.' As he went to lead her to the sitting-room, she drew back.

'I'd like to talk to you alone.'

Silently Roger held open the door of his study. 'I thought there was something up,' he said. 'Out with it.'

Tanya wondered how she could find out if Diana was here without actually asking, but her mind seemed lumpen and subtlety was impossible to come by; particularly when Roger repeated his earlier comment.

'Out with it, Tanya. What's wrong?'

'It's Diana,' she said swiftly. 'Is she here?'

Roger's astonishment could not have been simulated and it gave Tanya the answer she had feared. It also increased her fear for Diana's wellbeing.

'Why should she come here?' he demanded. 'If this is

another of your schemes to get us together——'

'It has nothing to do with me,' Tanya said hastily. 'But Diana's disappeared.'

'Disappeared?'

'She's gone. She quarrelled with her father yesterday and ran away. No one's seen her since.'

'What made you think she came here?'

'Because you were the reason she quarrelled with her father.'

'Now look,' Roger said forcefully, 'if you're making that up——'

'It's the truth. Her father as good as told me so when I spoke to him.'

Roger paced up and down, but could only take a couple of steps in either direction, which served to increase his impatience.

'Are you sure no one knows where she is?' he asked again.

'Positive. When I asked Lord Biddell to call the police, he said he wasn't worried.'

'He's too full of his own importance to worry about anyone!'

Tanya felt obligated to defend the old man. 'He said Diana rushed off in a tantrum and that she'd come back as soon as she'd cooled down. He could be right.'

'He could also be wrong. I'll go and see him myself. If he doesn't report it, then I will.'

'Would you like me to come with you?' she asked.

'No. It's better if you don't get involved.'

Hoping Roger and Lord Biddell would not come to blows, and wondering yet again whether she had done the right thing in going to see him, Tanya let Roger take her back to Park Gates, and even before she had opened the front door, he had driven away.

But it was an icily calm man who finally walked

across the floor of the huge library to come to a stop in front of the massive desk behind which Lord Biddell was sitting.

'Come to try and get my vote?' the older man asked.

'I'm here because of Diana. I'm worried about her.'

'Are you indeed! And what gives you the right to worry about my daughter?'

'The right of a man who happens to be concerned for her safety. I know she didn't come home last night and——'

'That foreign gel told you, I suppose?'

Roger's jaw clenched, but he still retained his control. 'I think you should go to the police.'

'And if I refuse?'

'Then I'll go to them myself.'

'Will you, be damned!' Lord Biddell roared. 'How dare you interfere in family matters? I've a good mind to have you thrown out!'

'That's just the answer I expected from you,' Roger said scathingly. 'You're so concerned for your own status that you don't give a damn for your daughter's safety!'

Lord Biddell's face was so suffused with colour that he looked as though he were about to have a stroke. With a great effort he recovered himself and, pushing his chair away from the desk, rose to his feet. 'If you're not out of here in two seconds,' he thundered, 'I'll throw you out myself!'

'Father!'

The two men swung round, surprise uppermost in their expressions as they saw Diana at the doorway.

'Where the devil have you been?' her father roared.

Without replying, she looked at Roger. 'Why are you and Father quarrelling?'

Roger went on staring at her as if he could not believe his eyes. 'Where have you been? Are you all right?'

'Of course I'm all right. But I'd like to know what's been happening.'

To Roger's ears her voice was so unbelievably calm—as if she'd only been out for a stroll instead of having disappeared for nearly twenty-four hours—that he lost his temper. 'Nothing's been happening. Nothing except that Tanya was worried sick in case you'd had an accident and I came here to persuade your father to call in the police.'

Diana blanched. 'The police? But I . . .' She looked dazed. 'I'd no idea anyone would worry about me.'

'Because you've got no feelings. You're your father's daughter all right! But next time you run off somewhere, have the decency to let Tanya know. Whatever you may think of *her*, she happens to be damn fond of *you*!' Roger strode forward, pushed her roughly out of the way, and a second later banged the front door behind him.

Diana drew a shuddering breath, but did not move until the sound of Roger's car died away.

'Well,' said her father, 'I'm waiting for an explanation.'

'I went away to think things over.'

'And left me to be the butt of that impudent young bounder! I've never had anyone talk to me like that.' He paused, arrested by the expression on his daughter's face. 'What are you looking so pleased about?'

'I wish I'd been here when Roger was speaking to you.'

'Where were you?' her father persisted.

'With Cousin Margaret.'

'Why didn't you let me know?'

'Because I didn't want you coming after me or bellowing at me down the telephone. I wanted a chance to think things out for myself.' Diana looked him fully in the face. 'I'm leaving home.'

'You'll do no such thing! This is your home and this is where you'll stay.'

'I won't. I'm tired of being treated like a child. I want to live my own life, and I can't do that if I stay here.'

Lord Biddell's skin took on a dull shade of puce. 'Who do I have to thank for this? Adrian's wife or Poulton?'

'It has nothing to do with either of them. It's my decision and no one else knows about it.'

'And where do you intend to live while you're making your own life?'

'With Aunt Margaret. At least till I've decided what to do.'

'You'll have to decide pretty quickly,' he told her. 'The minute you walk out on me, I'll stop your allowance.'

'I assumed you would.' Diana's hands were trembling and she hid them in the pockets of her dress. 'But it won't make me change my mind. I'm going to earn my own living.'

'You wouldn't even know where to start! The next thing you'll be telling me is you've taken a job scrubbing floors!'

'At least it would be honest work.'

'It's Poulton,' Lord Biddell thundered, his brief good humour vanishing without trace. 'He's the one who's made you think in this way. You were perfectly happy until you started seeing him again.'

'It has nothing to do with Roger.' Diana's face was strained, but her manner determined. 'For the first time I've made a decision for myself. I don't expect you to believe what I'm going to say now, but I want you to know that I—that I still love you and—and that I don't want to hurt you if I can help it. But I've got to live my own life.'

Lord Biddell pursed his lips and Diana waited, hoping for a sign of understanding.

'I can see I can't make you change your mind,' he said at last. 'You've got the bit between your teeth and the only thing for me to do is to give you your head. Go and get a job if you can. Try and stand on your own feet. You'll soon come running back to me.'

'Never!'

'Yes, you will. You don't know what it's like to live on a few pounds a week—not as pocket money, mind you, but as living money.'

'I'll learn,' she said shakily. 'It may be hard, but I promise you I'll learn.' She went to the door and then looked at him again, willing him to show he understood what she was trying to do. But he stared at her implacably, then painfully, arthritically settled himself back in his chair. Only then did Diana waver, longing to run over and tell him she would never leave him alone in his old age. But if she did she would be lost; lost not only for the present but also for the future. With a heavy sigh she turned and closed the door behind her.

In her room, she quickly packed her clothes. Roger's flowers stood in a vase on the dressing-table and she bent over them. Was it only yesterday that she had received them? Beneath the vase lay his card, and although she knew the words by heart, she read them again.

'Don't be like the violets that grow best when in the shade, but be like the roses that open themselves wide to the warmth of the sun.'

Well, she would show him she was no violet! But when she had shown him, what then? To Roger she would always represent a way of life he despised. Even if she made a life for herself, he would always see her as a poor little rich girl playing at being independent. How easy it was to visualise him in the years to come; following a successful Parliamentary career with a sensible, politically minded wife who would help him; a woman from the same background who would understand his way of thinking and agree with it.

But she was not taking this step because of Roger. She was doing it for herself. That was something she must never forget.

Back at Park Gates, Tanya waited in a fever of anxiety for Roger's call, but when a call did come for her it was from Diana.

'I'm sorry you were worrying about me, Tanya. I hadn't realised it until Roger told me.'

'You've seen him?' asked Tanya.

'Yes. He was with my father when I got home.'

'Is he still with you?'

'No, he left.' There was a pause. 'I'm leaving home,' Diana went on. 'I'll be staying with a cousin for a few weeks until I find a job.'

Tanya was lost for words. This was not what she had envisaged for Diana and Roger. What was the matter with them that they could not see they would only find happiness together?

'I'll call you when I've settled down,' Diana said. 'Then you can tell me whether you think I'm making a success of my life.'

'I am sure you will make a success,' Tanya replied. 'But I had hoped you and Roger——'

'Let's not go into *that*,' Diana cut in, and with an abrupt goodbye, put down the telephone.

Tanya stared at the receiver and wished it were Roger's neck, so that she could wring it from him. How could he let Diana go? Why hadn't he told her he loved her and asked her to marry him? Shaking her head, she went into the library, stopping in dismay as she saw Adrian there.

'I didn't know you were back.' She went to walk out, but a movement of his hand restrained her.

'Must you go?' he asked.

'I want to wash my hair.'

'It looks fine to me.' His eyes rested on the golden strands. 'Beautiful, in fact.'

She averted her head. 'Do you wish to talk to me about anything in particular?'

'Does it have to be something in particular before you'll agree to keep me company?'

'I'd rather you didn't ask questions like that.' Both her voice and her face were stony.

'You can't even pretend to like me, can you?'

She almost laughed at his question. Like him! What an inadequate word it was to describe the storm of love which the mere sight of him aroused in her. But with a calm for which she congratulated herself, she said:

'If you intend talking to me about the election, I will stay. But if you want to talk about the past, I will go.'

'I'm not interested in the past,' he said. 'Only the future.'

'My future will begin the day I leave here.'

Silently he reached out for a silver cigarette box.

'Aren't you smoking a lot?' she said involuntarily.

'I'll stop once the election is over.'

'What will you do if Roger wins?'

'Go back to managing my estate. I'm by no means sure I'd want to fight another seat.'

'Why did you agree to stand for Parliament in the first place?'

His hesitation was perceptible. 'Would you consider it

weak of me if I said I'd been influenced by the people around me?'

'We are all influenced by the people around us,' she said flatly. 'But the mark of a mature personality is to be able to make one's own decisions. Like Diana,' she added, deliberately changing the subject. 'She came back home.'

'Where was she?'

'With a cousin. She's going back to stay with her until she finds a job.'

'How much of that was her decision or yours?' he asked sarcastically.

'It was hers. One can influence but one cannot implement. The decision to leave home was Diana's entirely.'

'She isn't trained for anything,' he said.

'She is strong and she has a pair of hands. There is no disgrace in using them to earn your living. It is what I will do.'

'You've no need to——' He saw the look in the violet eyes and bit back the rest of his words.

'Please excuse me, Adrian,' Tanya said. 'I really do want to wash my hair.'

Left alone, Adrian stared moodily into space. In his mind's eye he followed Tanya to her bedroom, watched as she undressed and wondered if she still had the habit of carefully folding away her clothes but always leaving her stockings in a cobweb heap on the floor. A smile touched the corners of his mouth and his eyes grew tender as he imagined her unpinning the heavy coil of golden hair and letting it fall in a cloud to her waist.

It was impossible for him to believe there had ever been a time when he had stopped loving her, and he had forcibly to remind himself that he had managed to put her out of his mind sufficiently to become engaged to someone else. With hindsight he knew he had been prompted by a self-defence mechanism; a determination to forget the woman he had loved and who had divorced him—or so he had believed—by making another life for himself with someone else.

Now he knew how foolish that hope had been. No matter with whom he had lived, Tanya would always have haunted him. As she would continue to haunt him for the rest of his life.

'I can't let her go,' he thought. 'Everything I have is meaningless unless she's here to share it with me.'

CHAPTER FOURTEEN

ON polling day the weather was fair and Tanya accompanied Adrian on his visits to the various polling stations. All his helpers were supremely confident of his victory, and she had to remind herself that Roger's helpers were no doubt equally convinced he would win. If only it were possible for both men to be the victors! But she knew the hope was foolish and admitted she would feel deeply upset if Adrian lost. Was it because she did not believe him when he had said yesterday that he would prefer to look after his estate? No, she decided. It was because she did not want any other man to vanquish him. More than anything else, it told her how deeply she still loved him.

At seven o'clock they returned to the house for a light meal—neither of them having much appetite—and she asked Adrian if he wished her to return with him to the Committee Rooms.

'After all, in an hour the voting will be over and my being with you won't make any difference to the result.'

'I'd still like you to be there,' he replied. 'You've seen me through this far, so you might as well be in at the kill.' He gave a smile which held no amusement. 'I seem to have phrased that rather badly—or perhaps rather well.'

Silently Tanya went to her room to wash, knowing that had she replied, she would have given away her feelings. And she only had to hide them a short while longer. Soon the pretence would be over; the necessity for them to act as loving husband and wife gone.

Within the hour they were back to the mêlée and Tanya, watching the throng of canvassers and election campaigners who had been hard at work since seven o'clock that morning, felt guilty that she had not been out with them. But Adrian had expressly forbidden her to take an active part in his campaign and she wondered now, as she had wondered many times before, whether it was because she was a foreigner. That of course was one more reason why she wanted him to win; at least it would reassure her that in coming here, she had not spoiled his life.

At nine o'clock the polling booths closed and she and Adrian drove to the Town Hall to await the results. Vans were delivering ballot boxes and people were already counting the votes behind closed doors. Adrian seemed to have completely shed his earlier restlessness and he sat on a chair, his arms folded and his expression relaxed. Strangely enough he did not look tired either and his mouth was firmly set, as if he were already composing himself to face the verdict.

As if aware of her gaze he turned his head and, seeing her watching him, shifted his chair until he was closer to her. For the moment his head blocked out the rest of the room and they seemed to be completely alone. Tanya trembled, waiting for him to speak and not knowing what he was going to say. But when he did speak, the words were banal.

'You look tired, Tanya. Would you like me to fetch you a brandy?'

'No, thank you.' She felt herself drowning in the blueness of his eyes and searched for the proverbial straw. 'How soon do you think we will have the result?'

'Not for a few hours yet. It was an exceptionally heavy poll. I think that——' He jumped up as he saw a tall dark-haired girl pushing her way through the throng towards him. 'It's Diana,' he murmured, and went to greet her.

'Hello, Adrian,' she said with a faint smile. 'I had to come and wish you luck.'

'I'm glad you did. You worked like a Trojan throughout the campaign.' They went on looking at each other awkwardly and Tanya left her chair and joined them.

'It's good to see you, Diana. I was hoping you would come.'

'I'd have been here earlier, but I missed the first train and had to hang about for an hour.'

'So it's true you've left home,' Adrian said.

'Don't you think it's time I did?' Diana questioned, and then put up her hand to prevent Adrian answering. 'But I don't want to inveigle you into family quarrels.'

'I'd never think you were trying to do that. If I can help you in any way.... If you'd like me to speak to your father....'

Quickly Tanya moved out of earshot. It was only right for Adrian and Diana to talk alone. Her attempts to bring her and Roger together had come to nothing and she must now be prepared to have Diana turn back to Adrian. It was not too difficult to see them sharing their future together; never attaining the heights but never attaining the lows either. It might be the sort of life they both preferred.

'In a few months' time they will forget I ever came here,' Tanya thought wearily, and went to stand at the far side of the hall.

Left alone with Adrian, Diana did not know what to say to him. She was not sure if he knew exactly why she

had quarrelled with her father and she was reluctant—
ashamed even—to discuss her newly found feelings for
Roger.

'You *will* let me help you if you're ever in need of advice or money,' he said firmly. 'Though on the advice
side, I'm not sure I'd do a good job. I've not made a great
success of my own life.'

'Don't be silly. You weren't to blame for your
divorce.'

'I'm to blame for what's happened in the last few
months.'

'At the time, you did what you thought was right.'

'I've made two women unhappy,' he said tersely. 'You
and Tanya.'

'Not me,' Diana said quickly. 'Don't let's pretend
about *us*.'

'If your father hadn't always thrown me at you as an
ideal husband, you might have woken up to your real
feelings years ago.'

'I doubt it. I had to grow up first. And that's taken me
years.'

'And now you've grown up—what next?'

'I don't know. I don't want to think about it. From
now on my motto is one step at a time.' She glanced
round, but could not see Tanya. 'What about you, Adrian? Are you going to let Tanya leave you?'

Adrian's lids lowered to hide his eyes, then he raised
them as if having decided not to hide the truth. 'Until
today I'd made up my mind to fight for her, but—but in
the last few hours I've wondered whether she'd be happier if she were free of me.'

'Of course she wouldn't. I'm sure she loves you.'
Diana looked at her watch. 'I must go or I'll miss my
last train. Will you say goodbye to Tanya for me?'

'Why not stay the night with us?' he suggested.

'I'd rather not. If Father got to hear of it, he might see it as a sign of my repentance!'

Diana hurried away before she could give herself a chance to change her mind, though she almost did when she reached the street and saw it raining heavily. The wet pavements were treacherous for her high-heeled shoes and she stumbled twice and once went up to her ankles in a puddle. She wore no hat and soon her hair was plastered to her head. The weather was synonymous with her mood and the small rivulets of water trickling down her face mingled with the tears trickling from her eyes.

She had gone to the Town Hall in the hope of seeing Roger as well as Adrian, but a quick word with an official had told her he was remaining in his own Committee Rooms until shortly before the results were declared. So much for her hope of seeing him. But what would she have gained from another meeting? A declaration of love from him? If he had wanted to make it, he had had ample time to do so in the day she had spent at home while packing her clothes and arranging for them to be sent on to her cousin. She had even fought her pride sufficiently to tell the housekeeper that if Roger Poulton telephoned in her absence, he was to be given her new number and address. But there had been no word from him, and though she had tried to make herself believe it was because he was caught up in the excitement of polling day, logic would not let her accept it. Had his love for her been real and not some idealistic emotion that stemmed from his youth, nothing would have prevented him from calling her and saying how pleased he was that she had finally broken away from her father.

She stopped walking to wipe the rain from her face and saw she had taken the wrong turning. With an exclamation of annoyance she made for the short cut through the new shopping centre. Only as she did so did she realise she was passing Roger's Committee Rooms. The windows were plastered with posters showing his face and it brought him so close to her that she felt as though it were a physical contact. She stopped again, gasping for breath. Then on an impulse she could not deny, she stumbled through the door.

The room she entered was smoke-filled and full of people. They all seemed to be looking at her and she kept her face devoid of expression as she searched among the crowd for sight of the one man she wanted. But Roger was nowhere to be seen and she fumbled at the door handle, intent on escape.

'Diana! What are you doing here?'

She swung round and saw him making his way through the crowd. Under the fluorescent light his skin was greenish white, his hair redder than ever. The lines of strain on his face were so deeply marked they looked as though they had been carved into the flesh, while his eyes were red-rimmed from tiredness. Seeing him at his worst, Diana loved him the most and her heart contracted with tenderness for him.

'What do you want?' he repeated harshly.

'To—to see you b-before the result was announced,' she stammered, and for the very first time was no longer mistress of the situation.

Roger went on glaring at her, wishing that on this night when he was taxed to the uttermost, she had not decided to come and tax him further. The very sight of her was a torment that made him remember everything he wanted to forget; the satin-smoothness of her skin, the warmth of her breath, the touch of her lips. What a fool he had been to send her those flowers, to have expected some response from her.

Remembering her cool entry upon his angry scene with Lord Biddell, he writhed with embarrassment. She had probably gone to London to stay with one of her society friends, and must have been amused by the sight of his anxiety. Just because she had disappeared for a night! Determined never to show her any anxiety again, he strove to keep all feeling from his voice.

'It's kind of you to come and wish me luck, Diana. Or have you come to commiserate with me in case I lose?'

'Would you want my commiseration?'

'I want nothing from you.' He looked over his shoulder as someone at the end of the room called him. Diana turned the door handle and ran out.

Unfortunately it wasn't the door to the exit and she found herself in a gloomy corridor. For a moment she stood there, hating herself for the weakness that had made her come in search of Roger. She had hoped that if she made the first move to him, he would care sufficiently to make the second one. Well, now she knew better! Resolutely she searched for a way to get back to the exit without having to go through the main room again. There was another door on her left and she opened it and found herself in what she assumed was a canteen, for there was a counter at one end on which stood a mountain of cups and a large tea urn.

A depressed-looking woman, wiping some plates, looked at her in surprise. 'Tea's finished.'

'I don't want any. I'm trying to find my way out.'

'I'll show you,' said Roger behind her, and drawing her into the corridor, opened another door and pushed her unceremoniously into an empty office. Seeing her alone, he saw her clearly, and the muscles in his throat contracted. Gone was Diana's usual impeccable air. Her eyes were swollen and mascara was smudged across her cheeks. The rain had flattened her hair and a few dark locks splayed across her forehead. Only her mouth was as beautiful as ever; more beautiful in fact, for it was pale and trembling; soft and vulnerable.

Conscious of his gaze, she pulled her thin coat closely round her, shivering as the collar touched her neck.

'You're soaking wet,' he said.

'I won't melt.'

'Not ever?' He saw uncertainty on her face and tried to withstand his desire to comfort her. 'Your father won't approve of you coming here.' It was not what he had intended to say and he wondered if he were destined to ruin his own life because of his big mouth. 'I'm sorry for that,' he apologised. 'You *did* come, and I'm grateful for it.'

She looked around her. 'You were going to show me the way out.'

'Do you want me to?'

'What would you do if I said no?'

'This,' he replied, and wrapped his arms around her.

As he felt the closeness of her trembling body, Roger's last vestige of control vanished. Until tonight he had only shown Diana his anger and his desire, but now he showed her his need; openly declared that without her no victory was worth winning; no defeat more disastrous than the loss of her love.

'It won't be easy for us,' he whispered. 'Fighting this election will be child's play compared with the way I'll have to fight for you.'

'You've already got me,' she said. 'I've left home, Roger, and I'll come to you whenever you want.'

'Openly and proudly,' he said. 'It's the only way. And that means going back to your father.'

'Aren't you afraid he'll make me change my mind?'

Roger's answer was in the hard pressure of his mouth; the soft pressure of his moving hands; the burgeoning pressure of his thighs. Desire made her sag and he pushed her against the wall and kept her there by his weight.

'I want you,' she cried. 'Only you.'

'Then there's the answer to your question,' he said. 'And it's why I'm not afraid of *anyone*.'

CHAPTER FIFTEEN

WHEN Tanya looked at Adrian again, she saw that Diana had gone. Knowing herself to be unobserved, she allowed her eyes to feast on him, almost as if she were trying to absorb him into her consciousness. He was thinner than when she had first come to Park Gates and she wondered if this was due to her presence or to the exertion of the past months. Yet no matter how tired and irritable he was with others, he always tried to be polite to her. Too polite. Had their relationship been normal, he would have been able to allow himself to lose his temper or at least to show some of his feelings.

He turned to speak to the Mayor and though she was too far away to see his expression, she knew from his stance that he was making an immense effort to be calm. His head was bent forward, yet his shoulders were erect; his hands were held loosely at his sides, but the fingers were clenching and unclenching quickly. To most people he was an enigmatic man, but to Tanya he had always been easy to understand. Even as an eighteen-year-old she had not been in awe of him, recognising his reticence as shyness, his aloofness as a barrier that love could easily storm. And indeed love had done exactly that. The only trouble was that the love—on his part—had not lasted.

Suddenly she knew she could no longer remain here. Too overwrought to return to him and talk banalities, she left the hall and went into the street. It was raining hard and she waited on the steps of the Town Hall for

several moments until the downpour eased. Then she
began to walk, not knowing where she was going, only
knowing she could not be with Adrian.

The onset of the rain again, heavier this time, decided
her to seek shelter, and since shelter brought Roger
instantly to mind, she went in search of him. Besides, he
had been more of a friend to her than anyone else—
apart from Betty—and it seemed wrong that she should
not see him today and wish him well, even if he was
astute enough to know she wanted Adrian to win.

Only as she saw his headquarters ahead of her did she
hesitate. But another gust of rain precipitated her forward, and as she reached the entrance she saw a stream
of people moving out into the street, among them Diana.
In the same instant Diana saw her.

'Tanya!'

Tanya rubbed her hand over her forehead. 'It was so
hot—and the waiting, the suspense—no longer could I
bear it.'

'My dear, are you all right?'

'Yes. But I wanted to see Roger.'

'You've just missed him. He's already gone to the
Town Hall.'

The expression on Diana's face made Tanya tremble.
'Has he . . . do you mean he . . . he has won?'

'Yes. I'm terribly sorry. It was a very close thing, only
eight votes.'

'Oh, my poor Adrian!' Tanya turned away, but Diana
caught her arm.

'If you're going back to the Town Hall come with me.'

'I don't want to go back. I can't!' Pulling herself free,
Tanya hurried away, not pausing until she had turned
the corner and was hidden from sight. It was her fault
Adrian had lost. Until she had come on the scene every-

one had been confident of his victory. How he must hate her! And she could not blame him for it, when she hated herself. Well, he would never have to see her again. She would keep her word and leave Park Gates immediately.

Ignoring the rain, she ran to the taxi rank by the station and within twenty minutes was back at the house. It seemed empty and she guessed the staff were in their sitting-room listening to the television while the rest of the family were no doubt at the Town Hall with Adrian. Bitterly she smiled. Family on one side, she on the other. Alone, alone; always alone.

It was well after midnight when Adrian and the family returned to Park Gates and wearily went into the drawing-room, where drinks and sandwiches had been left for them. Quickly he poured himself a whisky and drained it, then strode into the library, expecting Tanya to be there. But the room was empty and he returned to the drawing-room.

'Is Tanya anywhere around?' he asked.

'She's probably gone to bed,' his mother replied. 'And a good thing too. She must feel so guilty that——'

'I won't have Tanya blamed for it!' he said harshly. 'My failure tonight had nothing to do with her. She might have cost me some votes in the beginning, but once she started campaigning with me, she gained more votes than she ever lost. People loved her. They could talk to her; they felt she was sympathetic.'

'You sound as if you're in love with her,' his mother sniffed.

'I'm glad you've finally realised it.'

Amazement held Mrs Chesterton rigid. Then she glanced from him to her daughter. 'I suppose you knew about it too?'

'Yes, Mother. And I think it's wonderful. Tanya's a lovely person.'

Unable to listen to any more discussion about his wife, Adrian made for the first floor. Outside Tanya's bedroom he stopped, debating what to do. He raised his hand to knock, but as he did so a clock downstairs chimed one and his hand fell to his side. It was too late to disturb her. He had wasted so much time that a few more hours would not matter.

At seven-thirty he was already downstairs, hovering impatiently in the hall for a sight of Tanya. But eight o'clock came and then half-past and there was still no sign of her. Moodily he went into the breakfast-room where he drank a cup of coffee and crumbled a piece of toast. He was on his second cup when Jean hurried in.

'Excuse me, sir, but do you know where Mrs Adrian is?'

'Isn't she in her room?'

'No, sir. And I don't think she was in it all night. I mean, her bed hasn't been slept in and the cupboard's half empty.'

'What!' Not waiting to hear any more, he took the stairs three at a time.

As Jean had said, the bed was still made and the cupboards were half bare. The glamorous evening dresses still hung there, but the bulk of her day-wear had gone. Hurriedly Adrian searched the room for a note, but found nothing. Roger! he thought suddenly. She had gone to Roger.

Without hesitation he went to his car. His mind refused to work beyond this point and he drove like an automaton, only returning to a semblance of life when he reached Roger's house and thumped on the door, the action helping to relieve some of his tension. He was still thumping on it when it was opened by a small boy who looked so much like Roger that Adrian knew it was his brother.

'Is Roger in?' he asked abruptly.

'Yes. You're Mr Chesterton, aren't you?'

'What's the trouble, Brian?' a voice called, and Roger came into view, stopping in surprise as he saw Adrian. He was too intelligent to pretend he thought it a social visit and at once led Adrian into the sitting-room. 'What's up?' he asked.

'I've come for Tanya.'

'Why here?'

'Because I know she's with you. Her bed wasn't slept in last night and her clothes have gone.'

'She's not here, I'm afraid. I only wish she were.'

'Do you, by God!'

'Only because we'd know where she was,' Roger said quickly. 'Tanya and I aren't emotionally involved.'

'I—I know that,' Adrian said jerkily. 'Forgive me if I'm not making much sense, but I—but I've got to find her. If she isn't here. . . .' His eyes narrowed. 'Of course, she must have gone to Tapley with Diana.'

'Diana didn't go back to Tapley last night. She stayed here.' Embarrassed, Roger thrust his hands into his pockets and said in a rush: 'Diana and I are engaged. My mother insisted she came back with us last night. She's in the kitchen now.'

Adrian was at a loss for words. He collapsed on to a chair and rested his head on his hands. 'So we still don't know where Tanya is.'

'As far away from here as possible, I should think,' Roger said bluntly. 'She as good as told me she'd leave here once the election was over. And when she heard you'd lost, she must have decided to go immediately.'

'How she must hate me,' Adrian said with deep bitterness.

'How she must love you,' Roger replied, and Adrian raised his head.

'You think so?'

'Don't tell me you didn't know!' Roger's expression veered between irritation and sympathy, and sympathy won. 'Good heavens, man, she's never stopped loving you. Why do you think she agreed to be nursemaid to your sister's children? To take her place as your wife when you finally decided it suited you to admit who she was? If she'd had an ounce of pride she'd have thrown back the offer in your face and walked out! The only reason she stayed was because she loved you, and if she's run away now, it's because she's given up hope of getting you back.'

'That can't be true!' Adrian jumped to his feet. 'Time and again I've tried to tell her how I feel, but she always fobbed me off.'

'Maybe she was afraid you were only going to make the best of things.'

Adrian groaned, remembering how many times he had used that expression to Tanya. No wonder she had doubted his feelings for her!

'I love my wife,' he said harshly. 'Wanting to start again had nothing to do with expediency. If I had to leave England in order to be with her, I'd go.'

'You should have told her,' said Roger.

'I wanted to wait till the election was over in case she felt I was using it as a ploy to keep her here.'

Roger nodded. 'I can see your reasoning, but it won't help us find Tanya.'

Adrian's shoulders sagged. 'She can't just disappear. She has no money and she's bound to go to one of the refugee organisations to help her.'

'She's got too much pride to ask anyone for help,' Roger said cuttingly. 'Surely you know her well enough to realise that?'

'I don't seem to have known her at all,' Adrian said bitterly.

The opening of the door made both men turn and Roger moved forward, arms outstretched, as Diana came in. Though she smiled at him, it was to Adrian that she went.

'I suppose Roger's told you the news,' she said.

He stared at her blankly, then with an effort, remembered and smiled. 'Yes, he has. Congratulations. I hope —I'm sure you'll be happy.'

'I know we will. If I can finally stand up to Father, I'm sure I can stand up to Roger.' She paused, her own pleasure fading as she realised that only extraordinary circumstances could have brought Adrian here. 'Something's happened to Tanya, hasn't it?'

'Yes. She's gone.'

'Surely it won't be difficult to find her?' Diana looked at Roger. 'I'm sure you've both got lots of contacts.'

'Not to find missing persons,' said Roger. 'The police are best for that.' He glanced at Adrian. 'Unless you don't want the publicity?'

'I don't give a damn about the publicity as long as I can find Tanya,' Adrian retorted. 'But let's look quietly first. If she finds out we're searching for her, she might go to ground so successfully we'll never find her.'

Never find her. They were words that echoed repeatedly in Adrian's brain as the days turned into weeks and the weeks into months.

Enquiries at the railway station elicited the fact that Tanya had caught the last train to London, and a porter at Victoria remembered a young woman with a suitcase getting off the train in the early hours of the morning and asking to be directed to the nearest tube station. After that the trail had been lost.

A well-known detective agency was brought in and when they finally admitted defeat, Adrian went to the police. But since he could not tell them he suspected foul play, they were unable to help, obviously regarding her flight from him as a wife's prerogative. In desperation he then contacted various refugee organisations, and though he received many names and addresses from them, none of them led to his wife.

He grew noticeably thinner and the flecks of grey at his temples became a definite silvering. He smiled less and less frequently and threw all his energies into the estate. But even this did not tire him and eventually he agreed to stand for Parliament in another constituency, hoping to forget his love by working himself to the maximum.

'You should ease up a bit,' Dick commented, one morning, as they drove in the Landrover to inspect various cottages.

'Work's my panacea,' Adrian replied. 'Without it, I don't think I could go on.'

'You love Tanya more now than when you married her,' Dick went on.

'I'm more of a man,' said Adrian, and hated himself because it was true; a truth that had come too late.

Christmas was the most dreary holiday he could remember spending. The effort to maintain an act in front of his family was more than he could cope with and on Boxing Day he went off on a skiing holiday. But though he had booked in at the resort for two weeks, he only had the patience to remain for one, and was glad to return to familiar surroundings, even though they reminded him of Tanya.

Tanya! She was like a fever in his blood that nothing could abate. It was only the fact that he was now living alone at Park Gates that made life tolerable, for at least when alone he had no need to pretend.

His mother had settled down in her cottage and had started to look up old friends around the country, while Betty was enjoying her new-found domesticity and had blossomed into an excellent cook.

'At last I feel I'm a wife and a mother,' she said one morning in mid-March, 'and I owe it all to Tanya.' The moment she spoke the name she looked dismayed and Adrian immediately put her mind at rest.

'Whether or not you talk about her makes no difference to my thinking of her,' he said.

'You think of her often?'

'All the time.'

'Poor Adrian!' she sighed.

'It's my own fault,' he said shortly.

'Have you considered the fact that you might never find her?'

'I daren't think of that. I'm living on hope. It's all I've got.'

Three days later Adrian's hope was justified when his solicitor, Mr Truscott, telephoned to say he had news of Tanya.

'She wrote to me yesterday,' he explained. 'She's worried that you might have had difficulty in terminating your marriage and wanted to know if there were any papers for her to sign.'

'Then you've got her address!' Adrian gave a jubilant shout. 'Where is she?'

'I can't tell you. She wrote to me in the strictest confidence.'

'I'll have you know you're *my* solicitor!' Adrian

stormed. 'And you also happen to be dealing with *my* wife. Do you understand that? My wife!'

'I am well aware of the position,' Mr Truscott replied with dignity.

'Then give me her address.' There was complete silence at the other end of the line. 'Look here, Truscott,' Adrian said quietly, 'you know I've been trying for months to find out where my wife is—not because I want to finalise my divorce but because I want to start my marriage again. If you prevent me seeing her, you'll be going against the law. Have you thought of that? You're supposed to do everything possible to get a couple together again!'

'That isn't strictly true, Mr Chesterton,' the lawyer replied, 'but I see your point.' There was another silence, broken by the wire crackling disapprovingly. 'I cannot see my way clear to breaking a confidence, but I see nothing remiss in telling you that Mrs Chesterton is in the Scilly Isles.'

'What the devil is she doing there?'

'I can't tell you that, but I gather she has been there some time.'

'I see. Thanks for your help, Truscott. I won't forget it.'

Adrian was on his way to the Scilly Isles an hour later.

CHAPTER SIXTEEN

THE plane throbbed through the sky and Adrian impatiently wished he could have commandeered a jet. At this rate it would be another hour before he touched down. Only Diana, whom he had met on the village station, knew where he was going, for she had sensed his inner excitement and guessed at the reason.

'You know where Tanya is?' she had said eagerly.

'At least I know where to start my search.'

'I hope things work out well for you.'

'No need for me to ask if they're working well for *you*. You look radiant.'

'I'm terribly happy.' She paused. 'Even happier today, because Father has agreed to welcome Roger.'

'I told you he would, given time. He didn't dance at your wedding, but I guaranteed he'd do so at the christening!'

'In eight months' time,' she confessed. 'You're the first to know.'

Adrian was astounded. 'It wasn't an inspired guess on my part. I was just making a joke.'

They had parted in London, Diana to return to her new home in Westminster, Adrian to make for the airport.

It was late afternoon when he reached Hugh Town, the capital of St Mary's, the largest of the Scilly Isles. The weather was so warm here that he took off his coat as he started to walk through the streets. The absence of cars made an almost tangible silence, and he wondered if this was why Tanya had come here. It was also about as far as she could get from Park Gates without actually leaving Britain, and his heart contracted as he digested this bitter idea. Well, assuming she had picked this place because it was the safest one in which to hide, what would be her first move when she arrived? To find somewhere to stay. He frowned. There were so many private boarding houses here that to visit each one was impossible. But after finding a place to live, she would want a job, and here he felt a greater surge of optimism. In a small place like this it should not be difficult to find a foreigner out of season.

By now he had reached the centre of the town and feeling thirsty, he went into a café for a drink. The woman who served him had the tanned skin of the habitual islander and her eyes were the same grey-blue as the surrounding water.

'Come for a holiday, sir?' she questioned as she set down the fresh orange juice he ordered.

'No. I'm——' He hesitated. The woman's eyes were so deep a colour that he was reminded of Tanya's, though hers were a different shade; and memory of Tanya made him blurt out the truth. 'It's my wife, actually. I'm looking for her. We quarrelled and she ran away.'

The woman looked sympathetic. 'When would that have been, sir?'

'Last autumn. But I'm not sure when she came here.'

'Have you tried the hotels?'

'She wouldn't have that sort of money. She's very proud and ... I'm sure she has a job.'

'Then like as not she'd have been sent to Mrs Tregar. The eyes and the ears of the Scilly Isles, that woman is. Always knows when anyone wants an extra pair of hands.'

Adrian paid for his drink. 'If you could tell me where to find her. . . .'

'I'll take you there myself,' the woman said, and led him a few yards down the street to an old-fashioned grocery shop where Mrs Tregar, a gnome-like woman with white hair and beady black eyes, presided behind a large brown counter covered with boxes of detergents and cornflakes.

'This gentleman is looking for his wife,' said the woman at Adrian's side. 'She's foreign and would have wanted a job.'

'Quite a few foreign girls come here looking for work.'

'She's blonde and wears her hair in a braid round her head,' Adrian said diffidently.

'Well now, why didn't you say so in the first place? 'Course I remember her. Hair like spun gold. Very beautiful young woman, if I may say so.'

'Do you know where she is?' Adrian asked.

'Can't say for sure. I gave her a couple of addresses. One was a guest house not far from the harbour. They wanted a maid, but I doubt if she went there or I'd have seen her in the town.'

'And the other address?' Adrian tried to hide his impatience.

'A flower farm on the other side of the island. You can walk it in half an hour. Mayfield, it's called. I'm sure she's there.'

Praying this would be the case. Adrian set off along the steep cliff road with the Atlantic swelling gently to his right. In the distance, looking gloomy and solitary, he could see the Penninis Head lighthouse, while to his left the landscape was dotted with cacti, aloes and prickly pear, giving the scene a tropical flavour that made it difficult to believe England was only a few miles away.

He breasted the highest point of the road and then began to descend until, turning past a clump of trees, he felt himself to be in fairyland. Surrounding him were fields of flowers, a confusion of colours that sprang like a rainbow out of the brown earth.

Pushing open a large double gate, he made his way through a vista of pink and yellow to a group of greenhouses. This was obviously Mayfield, and if his luck held out he would soon be seeing Tanya. What should he say to her? He ran his hand inside his collar and felt his skin to be damp. He was breathing heavily too and knew it had nothing to do with his brisk walk.

The scent of flowers was sickly in his nostrils and he wished he had spared the time to have something more substantial than an orange juice. It was crazy to rush halfway across England in search of his wife, only to fall down at her feet when he arrived.

He quickened his pace and then stopped, for coming towards him was a girl carrying an enormous armful of tulips, the same radiant gold as her hair. Her eyes were fixed lovingly on the blooms in her arms and she cradled them as if they were a child. Adrian's throat constricted and he would have given everything he possessed if, at that moment, it could truly have been a child in Tanya's arms—his child.

He murmured her name softly, and although she could not have heard his voice across the distance that separated them, some instinct told her she was being watched and she looked up and saw him. Her steps faltered and then slowly continued, not stopping again until she was a couple of yards away from him.

'So you are here. I should have known better than to trust your solicitor.'

'He only told me in what part of England you were,'

Adrian said quietly. 'And only then after I'd practically threatened him with murder! I came to St Mary's and took a chance I'd be able to find you.'

'Why do you want to?'

The question should have been an easy one to answer, but he could not bring himself to tell her he loved her. What would he do if she laughed at him? Until now he had lived with the hope of rebuilding their life together, but what life would he have if he were forced to live it alone?

'I must put the flowers down,' Tanya said. 'It is not good for them to be carried like this. If you will come into the greenhouse, we can talk.'

'Talk?'

'About the future. It is why you are here, is it not?'

Silently he followed her into the damp warmth of the greenhouse and watched as she set the tulips on a table. He saw a pile of boxes at her feet and noticed that several of them were already filled with blooms.

'You don't have to pack them, do you?'

'No. George—one of the men—does that.' She pointed to a rickety chair. 'It is not comfortable, but it is the best I can offer.'

'I don't want to sit down. I ...' Beads of sweat stood out on his forehead and Tanya saw them.

'It is hot for you in here,' she said matter-of-factly. 'Would you prefer it if we went outside?'

'No—yes—dammit, I don't know.'

'Why are you behaving so strangely, Adrian? You stare at me as if I am a ghost.'

'Perhaps you are. I've been searching for you for so long I can't believe I've found you. I keep imagining you'll disappear.'

Tanya shook her head. 'I am as real as the flowers.'

'But the flowers are picked and sent away,' he said jerkily, 'and if you go away I'll...' His control was slipping and the words inside him began to tumble out. 'How can you blame me for staring at you, when for months I've stared at every woman I've seen in the street, hoping against hope it might be you! You don't know what hell I've gone through since you left me. I've tried every possible means to find you, and when Truscott called me this morning and said he'd heard from you, I came here straight away.'

'You were so anxious?' she asked in a small voice.

'Did you think I wouldn't be?' He searched her face, wondering if Roger had been wrong in believing she loved him. She had shown no pleasure when she had seen him; made no movement of joy. Still, why should she welcome him when he had given her no welcome on the night she had arrived at his home?

'There was no need for you to come here.' She was speaking again. 'Everything could have been arranged through Mr Truscott.'

'I didn't come here to end our marriage. I came to ask you to begin it again.'

'No, thank you.'

There was no hesitation before she answered; not even the pretence of a momentary consideration. He was so shocked that he did not know what to say. Where was the love they had felt for one another? That wonderful pulsating emotion that had transformed two people from different backgrounds and position into one indivisible whole? But he and Tanya were no longer one; they were two separate entities with an ever-widening gulf between them.

He cleared his throat. 'If you won't come back to me, there's nothing more to be said.'

'Nothing. I'm sorry you had a wasted journey.'

She turned her back on him and began to place the tulips in a wooden box. Adrian blinked the moisture from his eyes and went to the door. He turned the handle, but it was stuck, the wood swollen with rain. He wrenched at it and, as it came towards him, he caught his finger on a jagged end of metal and ripped the skin on his thumb.

'Blast!' He drew back sharply and saw a spurt of blood. With his left hand he tried to get his handkerchief out of his pocket.

'You are hurt!' Tanya cried, and tried to take the handkerchief from him.

'Don't touch me!' he grated.

She paled and fell back. 'I'm sorry. I did not realise you hated me so much.'

'Hated you?' He gave a hollow laugh. 'If only I could!' He glanced at her in anguish and saw in her eyes a look that made his anguish recede. 'Don't you know I love you, Tanya? That the reason I can't bear you to touch me is because I want you so much?'

'*Want* me?' she echoed.

'Ironic, isn't it? First I reject *you*—and then you do the same to me.'

'I didn't know ... I never thought...' She took a deep breath. 'Why didn't you say all this when I was in your home?'

'And have you think I was doing it because of the election?' He remembered the times he had tried to tell her. 'I was waiting till it was all over—by which time you'd disappeared.'

'I see. I thought—when I saw you just now—that you wanted me back because Diana had married Roger.'

'What does that have to do with it?'

'It is easier for you to continue with me than to look for a new wife.'

'My God!' he said slowly. 'What sort of a swine do you take me for? I know I've behaved like one, but——'

'Please—do not criticise yourself.' She placed her hands on his chest. 'It is not good for a woman to hear bad things about the man she loves.'

His eyes glittered as if charged by electricity. 'Did you say *loves*?'

'The man I have always loved. Even when I said I hated you, I was lying. I will never love anyone else, Adrian, no matter whether you leave me or not.'

'I'll never leave you,' he groaned, and wasting no more time in words, sought for her mouth with a passionate eagerness that told her how much he had longed for her. But even as she responded to his kiss, he pushed her away from him.

'If I start now I won't be able to stop,' he said abruptly. 'And I dread what your George would say if he came in and found us crushing his beautiful tulips!'

'We could always pay him for them,' she murmured.

'I've a better suggestion. If we leave at once, we can get a helicopter flight home. Then I'll make a few calls and we'll be ready to go.'

'Where?'

'Anywhere you like. We'll continue with the honeymoon we were never able to finish.'

She looked at him with all her love in her eyes, seeing him as a supplicant before her; a defenceless, eager look on a face that until now had always been reserved. 'If only you had given me a sign how you felt,' she cried. 'We have wasted so many months!'

'Don't I know it! You've no idea the number of times I wanted to come into your room and make violent love to you.' He strained her close, pressing his body to hers. 'Sometimes I was in such torment I couldn't sleep. I used to pace the floor and curse myself for having so little control.'

'Too much control to give way to yourself,' she said, half seriously, half provocatively.

'My control's slipping now,' he said grimly. 'Don't keep looking at me like that. You don't know what it's doing to me.'

'I've a very good idea.' Her breasts swelled as she felt his body do the same, and then mutual need increased their desire. Their mouths came together and their passion diffused and widened, then intensified into a single dominant ache that only one action could assuage.

With a savagery that surprised and exulted her, Adrian pulled away her sun-dress. The buttons snapped and her creamy-skinned body was unfolded before him. Willingly she surrendered to his touch, linking her arms round his neck and pulling him further back into the greenhouse. Her own hands fluttered upon him, but shyness overcame her and with a soft murmur he caught them up and pressed them to his chest.

'Hold me,' he pleaded. 'Feel me ... Tanya!'

Coming round the side of the greenhouse, old George saw Tanya and a tall brown-haired man disappear from sight behind the wooden boxes that protected the lower half of the greenhouse. 'It's a good thing it in't all glass,' he chuckled into his beard. 'If t'were, I'd be learning a thing or two!'

Titles available this month in the Mills & Boon ROMANCE Series

LOREN'S BABY *by Anne Mather*
Why should Tristan Ross deny that he was the father of
Caryn's dead sister's baby? He was making himself responsible
for it, wasn't he?

IMAGE OF LOVE *by Rebecca Stratton*
Pablo had been no more than a friend to Rosanne, so why
should his death affect her relationship with the forbidding
Don Jaime Delguiro?

FOR BITTER OR WORSE *by Janet Dailey*
Stacy's husband Cord had become very embittered after an
accident which confined him to a wheelchair. Would his
attractive physiotherapist make things better or worse?

MIDNIGHT MAGIC *by Margaret Pargeter*
Maxine would never have let her stepfather persuade her to
use her charms on Nick Fleming if she had known where it
would lead her . . .

LOVE FOR A STRANGER *by Jane Donnelly*
It was only after Louise had committed herself to marrying
Tom Reading that she realised she didn't know the first thing
about him!

LORD OF THE ISLAND *by Mary Wibberley*
Luke Vilis had blackmailed Sally into marrying him — but
how could their marriage ever work when the ghost of his
dead wife kept reappearing?

UNDER MOONGLOW *by Anne Hampson*
Half an island in the Seychelles was Reyna's delightful legacy
— but then she hadn't met the mysterious Thor Granville who
owned the other half!

BELOVED SURGEON *by Sheila Douglas*
Luke Haddon was the R.S.O. and Jill Bentley only a humble
junior surgeon — so wasn't she wasting her time thinking
seriously about him?

THE GOLDEN GIRL *by Elizabeth Ashton*
Adrien Belmont never seemed to see Rosamund as a woman —
and why should he, when he was going to marry the
sophisticated Madeleine?

UNWANTED WIFE *by Rachel Lindsay*
(A Time to Love)
Years after her accidental separation from her husband, Tanya
was to find him again - engaged to another girl!

Mills & Boon Romances
— all that's pleasurable in Romantic Reading
Available May 1978 — Only 50p each

Also available this month
Four Titles in our Mills & Boon
Classics Series

*Specially chosen re-issues of the best in
Romantic Fiction*

May's Titles are:

DARE I BE HAPPY?
by Mary Burchell

Marigold should have been blissfully happy in her marriage
to Paul Irving — but how could she, when the one man in the
world who could wreck it with a word was Paul's own
brother-in-law?

THE CASTLE OF THE SEVEN LILACS
by Violet Winspear

When the handsome Baron Breck von Linden offered Siran
a job which involved staying at his fairytale home, the
Castle of the Seven Lilacs, she knew that it was attraction
for the Baron that was taking her there. But Breck's younger
brother Kurt made no secret of his opinion of Siran and
her motives. . . . .

A MAN WITHOUT MERCY
by Margery Hilton

Compassion and loyalty — two endearing qualities, but they
had brought Gerda nothing but heartbreak. Compassion had
led her into a brief, tragic marriage. Now loyalty had forced
her into the power of the one man who could destroy her.
Because she loved Jordan Black as much as he despised her
— and he was a man without mercy . . . . .

SOUTH TO FORGET
by Essie Summers

After an unhappy love affair Mary Rose wanted to get away
from everything, so when Ninian Macandrew, who had also
recently been jilted, asked her to go to his New Zealand
home with him as his fiancée it seemed the solution to her
problems. But "Oh what a tangled web we weave, when
first we practise to deceive"!

Mills & Boon Classics
— all that's great in Romantic Reading!
BUY THEM TODAY only 50p

We are pleased to announce

that we will be launching Masquerade Historical
Romances as a monthly series from July 1978.
Four titles will be published in July, followed by
two titles a month from August onwards.
The July titles will be:

SOPHIE AND THE PRINCE
Sylvia Sark

The sweet and gentle Sophie Johnson travels to pre-
revolutionary Russia to be English teacher to the daughters
of the dynamic Prince Peter Rasimov. There she falls
deeply in love with him, but wonders how she can overcome the difference in their backgrounds and deal with
the treachery of the scheming French governess . . . .

THE DEVIL'S DAUGHTER
Marguerite Bell

As companion to his wards, Harriet Yorke does not hesitate
to confront the Marquis of Capel when he neglects them.
Her appearance at the scene of a duel almost causes his
death, but gentle nursing does nothing to make her obstinate
patient alter his low opinion of her. Is jealousy the answer?

MADELON
Valentina Luellen

Travelling to court in 11th century Spain, the beautiful
Madelon and her brother Pedro are captured by fierce
Moors. Almost enslaved, their rescue comes unexpectedly
from the noble and magnificent Valentin Maratin, her
brother's sworn enemy . . . . . .

STRANGER AT THE GATE
Frances Lang

After years of exile in Holland, Clemence de Frainville's
brother unexpectedly returns to his family chateau in
France. Clemence is initially puzzled when she does not
recognise Edouard, and then angered when he forbids her
to marry the handsome Armand.

Great Value at only 60p

CUT OUT AND POST THIS PAGE TO RECEIVE

FREE

FULL COLOUR
Mills & Boon
CATALOGUE

and – if you wish – why not also ORDER NOW any (or all) of the favourite titles offered overleaf?

Because you've enjoyed *this* Mills & Boon romance so very much, you'll really *love* choosing more of your favourite romantic reading from the fascinating, sparkling full-colour pages of "Happy Reading" – the *complete* Mills & Boon catalogue. It not only lists ALL our current top-selling love stories, but it also brings you *advance news* of all our exciting NEW TITLES *plus* lots of super SPECIAL OFFERS! And it comes to you complete with a convenient, easy-to-use DIRECT DELIVERY Order Form.

Imagine! No more *waiting*! No more "sorry – sold out" disappointments! HURRY! Send for *your* FREE Catalogue NOW . . . and ensure a REGULAR supply of all your best-loved Mills & Boon romances this happy, carefree, DIRECT DELIVERY way! But why wait?

Why not – *at the same time* – ORDER NOW a few of the highly recommended titles listed, for your convenience, *overleaf*? It's so simple! Just tick *your* selection(s) on the back and complete the coupon below. Then post *this whole page* – with your remittance (including correct postage and packing) for speedy *by-return* despatch.

✱ **POST TO: MILLS & BOON READER SERVICE, P.O. Box 236, 14 Sanderstead Road, S. Croydon, Surrey, CR2 0YG, England**
Please tick ☑ (as applicable) below:–

☐ Please send me the FREE Mills & Boon Catalogue

☐ As well as my FREE Catalogue please send me the title(s) I have ticked ☑ overleaf

I enclose £................................ (No C.O.D.) Please add 8p. postage and packing per book. (*Maximum Charge: 48p for 6 or more titles*)
Please write in BLOCK LETTERS below

NAME (Mrs./Miss)..

ADDRESS ....

CITY/TOWN...

COUNTY/COUNTRY..POSTAL/ZIP CODE..................

✱ *S. African and Rhodesian readers please write to:*
P.O. Box 11190, Johannesburg, 2000, S. Africa. X1/1386

ORDER NOW FOR DIRECT DELIVERY

Choose from this selection of

Mills & Boon 🌹
FAVOURITES
—*ALL HIGHLY RECOMMENDED*

☐ 1334
BREEZE FROM THE BOSPHORUS
Elizabeth Ashton

☐ 1344
PLANTATION MOON
Gloria Bevan

☐ 1338
THE SILVER TREE
Katrina Britt

☐ 1331
REILLY'S WOMAN
Janet Dailey

☐ 1337
TO TELL THE TRUTH
Janet Dailey

☐ 1343
TOUCHED BY FIRE
Jane Donnelly

☐ 1330
BELOVED VAGABOND
Anne Hampson

☐ 1341
TO PLAY WITH FIRE
Flora Kidd

☐ 1347
HAWK IN A BLUE SKY
Charlotte Lamb

☐ 1329
NOT A MARRYING MAN
Roberta Leigh

☐ 1333
THE TIME AND THE LOVING
Marjorie Lewty

☐ 1345
DEVIL IN VELVET
Anne Mather

☐ 1340
LURE OF THE FALCON
Sue Peters

☐ 1342
LION OF VENICE
Margaret Rome

☐ 1335
ADAIR OF STARLIGHT PEAKS
Essie Summers

☐ 1336
CARIBBEAN ENCOUNTER
Kay Thorpe

☐ 1332
MUTINY IN PARADISE
Margaret Way

☐ 1328
DAUGHTER OF THE SUN
Mary Wibberley

☐ 1339
WILD GOOSE
Mary Wibberley

☐ 1327
TIME OF THE TEMPTRESS
Violet Winspear

ONLY 40p EACH

SIMPLY TICK ☑ YOUR SELECTION(S) ABOVE, THEN JUST COMPLETE AND POST THE ORDER FORM OVERLEAF ▶